THE GAME GROWN-UPS JUST CAN'T WIN

ULTIMATE TRIVIA

THE BOOK YOU PLAY!

KIDS' STUFF

COMPILED BY
GARFIELD REEVES-STEVENS
WITH
CAMPBELL KINGSBURGH
AND
STEVE HEASLIP
SPECIAL RESEARCH
ADRAY VELCHEFF

PINNACLE BOOKS  NEW YORK

Special thanks to Cynthia Good of Penguin Books Canada for her help in developing the rules of the game.

Thanks also to award-winning rider Gregory Velcheff for revealing the secrets of BMX.

ULTIMATE TRIVIA: KIDS' STUFF

A Pinnacle Books edition, published by special arrangement with Penguin Books Canada, Limited.

Penguin edition published in 1984
Pinnacle edition/June 1985

ISBN: 0-523-42560-0
Can. ISBN: 0-523-43505-3

Printed in the United States of America

PINNACLE BOOKS, INC.
1430 Broadway
New York, New York 10018

9 8 7 6 5 4 3 2 1

Dedicated with much love to the newest kids in town:
Jordan Stevens and Glynis Kestell Tabor!

INTRODUCTION

Of the more than 2,000 questions in this book, there is at least one which you, and every other kid in the world, have already asked:

Why is it that I have to struggle to memorize the capitals of the states, the voyages of Magellan, and the parts of a flower when I can remember my first ten scores in *Dragon's Lair*, all the lyrics to the whole *Thriller* album, and every alien shown in *Star Wars* without even trying?

You want to know why?

It's because nobody *told* you to remember *Dragon's Lair*, *Thriller*, and *Star Wars*.

Nobody told you there'd be a test on dragon slaying. Nobody asked you to write an essay on the use of imagery in Michael Jackson's lyrics, and nobody made you prepare a report on the ecology of moisture farms on Tatooine.

Instead, you learned all of that stuff—or at least most of it—just because you *liked* it.

That's what makes this book so much fun. Almost every question in it involves something you don't *have* to know because almost all the questions are about the things you like and *want* to know.

In fact, there's only *one* thing that someone can tell you to do with it—and that's to have fun.

P.S. If you're sick and tired of being roped into one of those other trivia games with adults—you know, the ones with questions about things that only people with gray hair know about—get an adult to play *this* game with you. It's guaranteed to teach anyone over fourteen some humility.

HOW TO PLAY

YOU WILL NEED

This Game Book
At least one pencil or pen
One ordinary six-sided die

The Game Book has more than 2,000 questions and answers and eight Scoresheets.

The Scoresheets are at the back of the book. Photocopy as many as you want or just write the letters **T. R. I. V. I·. A.** down a sheet of paper three times for each player.

HOW TO START

Each player rolls the die once. Since this is a game of trivia, the player rolling the *smallest* number goes first. If two or more players are tied, then those players roll again.

QUESTIONS AND ANSWERS

The player throws the die three times to pick a Question Page. Each right-hand page in the book has three sets of six questions. The three numbers of the roll show which Question Page to turn to. The Question Page numbers are the dark numbers in the bottom right-hand corner of each set of questions. If someone rolls **4-2-5,** then turn to the question page with that number.

The player rolls again for a fourth number; this shows which of the three sets of questions to use. **A 1** or a **2** means the top questions; **3** or **4,** the middle; and **5** or **6,** the bottom. Those numbers appear in the *upper* right-hand corner of each set of questions.

When the book is open to the proper set of questions, the player whose turn it is names her or his first choice for a *subject*: **T, R, I, V, I·,** or **A.** (The subjects that belong to each letter are shown on the page preceding the first page of questions.) Then the player reading the questions tells how many points that question is worth. The points are in parentheses following each question. Questions can be worth between 1 and 6 points depending on their difficulty: those worth 1 point are relatively easy; 6-pointers may be quite difficult. Some questions are so hard they are called Devastators—the rules for these are explained later in this section.

The player whose turn it is may then ask for a new subject or ask to have the question read. NOTE: *A player should never hear a question before deciding whether or not to answer it*. Once a question has been read out loud, the player whose turn it is must try to answer.

If you want to have a time limit, each player should agree on it before the game starts. One minute is a fair limit.

After the player gives an answer, the reader turns over the Question Page to read the answer on the back. (Some answers have extra facts in parentheses. A player does not have to give the extra facts to get full points.) Players should try very hard not to read other answers on the page.

If the answer is right, the player writes the number of points the question was worth beside the subject letter on her or his Scoresheet. NOTE: *The player may not answer another question in that subject until she or he has correctly answered a question in every other subject.*

The player on the right goes next.

If the answer is wrong, the reader gives the correct answer and no points are scored.

Players can take a second turn only if they have tried to answer a Devastator question. Otherwise, the player on the right goes next.

WINNING

The first player to score 13 points wins.

Players may score more than 13 points if the winning question is worth more points than they need.

TIPS

The more points a question is worth, the more difficult it is to answer. If "Movie Stuff" is your best subject, wait until you choose a question set with a **T** question worth 5 or 6 points so you can get a high score. If **T** is your worst subject, try to answer **T** questions worth 1 or 2 points because they will be the easiest.

Remember, players cannot answer a second question in any subject until they have correctly answered a question in every other subject. The same rule goes for a third question, if one is needed. (This would only happen if someone answered two questions worth one point each in all six subjects.)

DEVASTATOR QUESTIONS

Some questions have the letter D instead of a number in the parentheses. Because these are so difficult, a player is allowed to take another turn if she or he does not answer correctly. Any player who does answer a Devastator correctly scores 8 points *and* takes another turn.

HANDICAPPING

When older kids play with younger kids, or kids who know a lot of trivia play with kids who have never played a trivia game before, make the game more interesting and competitive by requiring the more experienced or older players to get a higher score to win. Try 16 or 20 points.

You can also have some players choose from fewer subjects—either their best or their worst—to make the game even and more fun.

USING QUESTION SETS WITH OTHER GAMES

If you already have a trivia game but know all the answers, or if you want to play with new subjects, this book can be used easily with most other games. See the last page in the book for instructions on how to cut the pages into game cards.

You may wish to remove the pages with the Rules and Scoresheets on them before cutting up the book so you can keep playing this game, too.

A FINAL WORD

Have fun and don't take it too seriously. After all, if you're no good at trivia, it just proves you were made for bigger things!

SUBJECTS

T	Movie Stuff
R	Television Stuff
I	Comics Stuff
V	Fun Stuff
I	School Stuff
A	Grab Bag

1 OR 2

T. Who ya gonna call?(1)
R. In what show do Tess and Dan ride around in Wheels and Roadie?(3)
I. What are the colors in the *S* symbol on Superman's chest?(2)
V. What are the nicknames of the monsters in the *Pac-Man* video game?(4)
I·. Who was the second person to walk on the Moon?(6)
A. Who is older, Donald Duck or Mickey Mouse?(5)

QUESTIONS 111 and 112

3 OR 4

T. In the first three *Star Wars* movies, how many Death Stars were built?(4)
R. Who are the *Star Trek* aliens who look like Vulcans but have emotions?(5)
I. What comic-strip character has a dog named Sandy?(3)
V. What was the first video game to feature interactive video-disk animation?(2)
I·. When it is −40° Fahrenheit, what temperature is it in degrees Celsius?(6)
A. How many pieces of bun are there in a Big Mac?(1)

QUESTIONS 111 and 112

5 OR 6

T. What can't Superman's X-Ray vision see through?(1)
R. Whose movie spaceship appears in the opening credits of *Muppet Babies*?(5)
I. In *Superman* comics, what planet does Superhorse come from?(6)
V. What was the name of the first company to make video games?(3)
I·. How many days are in a leap year?(4)
A. Who is the Mayor of McDonaldland?(2)

QUESTIONS 111 and 112

1 OR 2

T. Ghostbusters!
R. *Pole Position*
I. Red and yellow
V. Inky, Blinky, Pinky, and Clyde
I+. Edwin "Buzz" Aldrin
A. Mickey (by six years)

111 and 112 ANSWERS

3 OR 4

T. One (The second Death Star was destroyed before it was completed)
R. Romulans
I. Little Orphan Annie
V. *Dragon's Lair*
I+. −40° (This is the only temperature at which the two scales are the same)
A. Three

111 and 112 ANSWERS

5 OR 6

T. Lead
R. Darth Vader's
I. Earth (Superhorse is a human who has been enchanted by the sorceress Circe)
V. Atari
I+. 366
A. Mayor McCheese

111 and 112 ANSWERS

1 OR 2

T. With whom did Luke Skywalker live on his home planet of Tatooine?(3)
R. What does Porky Pig say at the end of cartoons?(2)
I. What color is Superman's cape?(1)
V. What is usually considered to be the very first video game?(5)
I·. What is the day that is added in a leap year?(4)
A. How many Walt Disney theme parks are there?(6)

QUESTIONS 113 and 114

---

3 OR 4

T. Who is Luke Skywalker's sister?(1)
R. What is the name of Petunia Pig's boyfriend?(2)
I. What is the name of Richie Rich's butler?(3)
V. In baseball, what happens when the batter is hit by a wild pitch?(5)
I·. What is the capital of Mexico?(4)
A. Mr. T bases his haircut on the style of which African tribe?(D)

QUESTIONS 113 and 114

---

5 OR 6

T. By what name was Annikin Skywalker better known?(1)
R. What animated duck is known for saying "Woo-woo! Woo-woo!"?(3)
I. What is the name of the dog that Garfield the Cat likes to beat up?(2)
V. What do people in North America call the game that people in England call football?(4)
I·. On what area of the moon did the first people land?(D)
A. What would you call someone who had lycanthropy?(5)

QUESTIONS 113 and 114

1 OR 2

T. His aunt and uncle (Aunt Beru and Uncle Owen)
R. "Th-th-th-that's all folks!"
I. Red
V. *Pong*
I+. February 29
A. Four (Disneyland, Tokyo Disneyland, and two at Walt Disney World—The Magic Kingdom and the Experimental Prototype Community of Tomorrow)

113 and 114 ANSWERS

3 OR 4

T. Princess Leia
R. Porky Pig
I. Cadbury
V. The batter walks
I+. Mexico City
A. The Mandinka Tribe

113 and 114 ANSWERS

5 OR 6

T. Darth Vader
R. Daffy Duck
I. Odie
V. Soccer
I+. The Sea of Tranquillity
A. A werewolf

113 and 114 ANSWERS

1 OR 2

T. Name the two regular pilots of the *Millenium Falcon.*(2)
R. What animated duck stars as *Duck Dodgers in the 24th-and-a-half Century*?(3)
I. What is Superman's secret identity?(1)
V. In what game will you find a scrum?(6)
I+. What is the largest animal ever to have lived on the planet Earth?(5)
A. What do you get one year after you "adopt" a Cabbage Patch Kid?(4)

QUESTIONS 115 and 116

3 OR 4

T. In the movie *Star Wars*, what is Old Ben's full name?(3)
R. Who is always saying "I'm going to get that wabbit?"(2)
I. Who is known as The Poor Little Rich Boy?(1)
V. What game originally was included with the Adam computer?(4)
I+. How often must there be a Presidential election?(5)
A. What do the initials NASA stand for?(6)

QUESTIONS 115 and 116

5 OR 6

T. In the movie *Star Wars*, which robot had the secret message from Princess Leia?(2)
R. Is Elmer Fudd a cartoon person or a cartoon rabbit?(1)
I. Who is known as The Boy Wonder?(5)
V. In the *Pac-Man* game, how many Energizers are there in each screen that will let Pac-Man eat the monsters?(4)
I+. What state is known as the Golden State?(6)
A. What group did Paul McCartney play for before he played for Wings?(3)

QUESTIONS 115 and 116

1 OR 2

T. Han Solo and Chewbacca
R. Daffy Duck
I. Clark Kent
V. Rugby
I+. Blue Whale
A. A birthday card

115 and 116 ANSWERS

---

3 OR 4

T. Obi-wan Kenobi
R. Elmer Fudd
I. Richie Rich
V. *Buck Rogers Planet of Zoom*
I+. Every four years
A. National Aeronautics and Space Administration

115 and 116 ANSWERS

---

5 OR 6

T. R2-D2
R. A cartoon person
I. Robin
V. Four
I+. California
A. The Beatles

115 and 116 ANSWERS

1 OR 2

T. In the movie *Superman*, what letter did Superman's father wear on his chest?(4)

R. In *Peanuts* cartoons, who is in love with the little red-headed girl?(3)

I. In what city does Superman live?(1)

V. Which two properties are the least expensive in *Monopoly*?(5)

I+. The very first NASA space shuttle to be built never went into space; what was its name?(D)

A. For which group is Boy George the lead singer?(2)

QUESTIONS 121 and 122

---

3 OR 4

T. In the movie *Superman*, what did Superman catch after he caught Lois Lane?(5)

R. In *Peanuts* cartoons, what is the name of the little boy who always carries a blanket?(3)

I. What is the name of Richie Rich's girl friend?(4)

V. What is the name of the knight in *Dragon's Lair*?(6)

I+. What is the capital of the United States?(1)

A. When does a werewolf come out?(2)

QUESTIONS 121 and 122

---

5 OR 6

T. In the movie *Superman*, what newspaper did Clark Kent work for?(1)

R. In *Peanuts* cartoons, who is the little boy who always plays the piano?(4)

I. What color is Superman's belt?(5)

V. What is the name of the princess in the *Dragon's Lair* game?(6)

I+. What is another term for "terrible lizards"?(3)

A. What do the initials UFO stand for?(2)

QUESTIONS 121 and 122

1 OR 2

T. The letter S
R. Charlie Brown
I. Metropolis
V. Mediterranean and Baltic avenues
I+. The *Enterprise*
A. Culture Club

121 and 122 ANSWERS

---

3 OR 4

T. A helicopter
R. Linus
I. Gloria
V. Dirk the Daring
I+. Washington (District of Columbia)
A. When the moon is full

121 and 122 ANSWERS

---

5 OR 6

T. *The Daily Planet*
R. Schroeder
I. Yellow
V. Daphne
I+. Dinosaurs
A. Unidentified Flying Object

121 and 122 ANSWERS

1 OR 2

T. In the *Rocky* movies, what was Rocky's last name?(3)
R. In *Peanuts* cartoons, what color is Woodstock?(1)
I. What superpower does Superman use to see through walls?(2)
V. How many times can the knight die before a single game of *Dragon's Lair* is over?(4)
I+. When water freezes, does it expand or contract?(5)
A. What do the initials C.O.D. stand for?(6)

QUESTIONS 123 and 124

---

3 OR 4

T. What secret agent is known by the number 007?(1)
R. What cartoon dog was born at the Daisy Hill Puppy Farm?(3)
I. What is the name of Richie Rich's red-haired best friend?(6)
V. In the *Pac-Man* video game, who travels faster in the warp tunnels, Pac-Man or the monsters?(5)
I+. What planet is closest to the sun?(2)
A. On what side of the road do people drive their cars in England?(4)

QUESTIONS 123 and 124

---

5 OR 6

T. What country does James Bond work for?(6)
R. In *Peanuts* cartoons, who owns Snoopy?(2)
I. What color is Richie Rich's bow tie?(3)
V. What color is Pac-Man?(1)
I+. What is the most southerly continent on Earth?(4)
A. In computers, what does RAM stand for?(5)

1 OR 2

T. Balboa
R. Yellow
I. X-Ray vision
V. Three times
I+. It expands
A. Cash on Delivery

123 and 124 ANSWERS

3 OR 4

T. James Bond
R. Snoopy
I. Freckles
V. Pac-Man
I+. Mercury
A. The left-hand side

123 and 124 ANSWERS

5 OR 6

T. England
R. Charlie Brown
I. Red
V. Yellow
I+. Antarctica
A. Random Access Memory

1 OR 2

T. Where did James Bond fly to at the end of the movie *Moonraker*?(3)
R. In *Peanuts* cartoons, who pretends he is fighting The Red Baron?(2)
I. What color are the polka dots on Little Dot's dress?(4)
V. Who "runs" a *Dungeons and Dragons* game?(5)
I⁺. Who was the first President of the United States?(1)
A. What is the Harley-Davidson Company most noted for making?(6)

QUESTIONS 125 and 126

---

3 OR 4

T. By what letter was James Bond's boss called?(4)
R. In *Peanuts* cartoons, what is the name of the little boy who is always dirty?(2)
I. In *Harvey* comics, what is the name of the big little girl who likes to eat?(3)
V. In *Dungeons and Dragons*, which color dragon is usually the most powerful?(6)
I⁺. What were the last two states to join the United States?(5)
A. In what magazine does Alfred E. Neuman appear?(1)

QUESTIONS 125 and 126

---

5 OR 6

T. What did the man called Q make for secret agent James Bond?(5)
R. In *Peanuts* cartoons, what is the name of the little girl who keeps moving the football away from Charlie Brown?(1)
I. What color was the sun of Superman's home planet?(3)
V. What is the name of the Queen of England?(4)
I⁺. What animal is on the back of a quarter?(2)
A. In *The Hobbit*, what riddle did Bilbo ask Gollum which Gollum couldn't answer?(6)

QUESTIONS 125 and 126

1 OR 2

T. Space station (or outer space)
R. Snoopy
I. Black
V. The Dungeon Master
I+. George Washington
A. Motorcycles

125 and 126 ANSWERS

3 OR 4

T. M
R. Pigpen
I. Little Lotta
V. Gold
I+. Hawaii and Alaska
A. *MAD*

125 and 126 ANSWERS

5 OR 6

T. Special guns and other weapons
R. Lucy
I. Red
V. Elizabeth (the Second)
I+. An eagle
A. "What do I have in my pocket?"

125 and 126 ANSWERS

1 OR 2

T. On what kind of dragon did Bastian fly in *The Neverending Story*?(2)
R. Where does Snoopy like to sleep?(3)
I. In what town does Superboy live?(6)
V. How many sides are there on a standard die?(1)
I+. In what year did the United States first become a country?(4)
A. Does a dolphin have a bellybutton?(5)

QUESTIONS 131 and 132

3 OR 4

T. What was the name of the movie in which Harrison Ford played a policeman in the future who had to hunt runaway artificial humans?(6)
R. What is the name of Mr. T's cartoon show?(5)
I. When Bruce Wayne puts on his mask and cape, who does he become?(4)
V. In the *Donkey Kong* game, what does the ape roll at your player during the ramp screen?(2)
I+. How many years are in a century?(1)
A. How many stripes are on the side of an Adidas running shoe?(3)

QUESTIONS 131 and 132

5 OR 6

T. In the movie *Blade Runner*, who drove the flying cars called spinners?(6)
R. In his cartoon show, what kind of a coach is Mr. T?(5)
I. What is the name of The Batman's car?(2)
V. In the *Donkey Kong* game, what can your player use to destroy hazards during the ramp and the rivet screens?(3)
I+. How many years are in a decade?(4)
A. What company makes camera film that comes in yellow boxes?(1)

QUESTIONS 131 and 132

1 OR 2

T. A Luckdragon
R. On top of his doghouse
I. Smallville
V. Six
I+. 1776
A. Yes (Dolphins are mammals)

131 and 132 ANSWERS

3 OR 4

T. *Blade Runner*
R. *Mr. T*
I. The Batman
V. Barrels
I+. One hundred
A. Three

131 and 132 ANSWERS

5 OR 6

T. Police officers
R. A gymnastics coach
I. The Batmobile
V. Hammers
I+. Ten
A. Kodak

131 and 132 ANSWERS

1 OR 2

T. In the movie *Blade Runner*, what computer-game company had an advertising sign?(2)
R. On Mr. T's cartoon show, what's the name of the little kid who tries to act just like Mr. T?(5)
I. What does Superboy's foster father do for a living?(3)
V. What game won the award for Best Science Fiction/Science Fantasy Game of the Year in 1984?(6)
I+. What is the hardest natural substance on Earth?(1)
A. What substance in popping corn makes it pop?(4)

QUESTIONS 133 and 134

3 OR 4

T. In the movie *E.T.*, what game did Elliot and his brother play with their friends?(4)
R. Who has three nephews named Huey, Louie, and Dewey?(1)
I. What is the name of Superboy's dog?(3)
V. How many arms does the Pentapus have in the game of the same name?(5)
I+. Of the North Pole and the South Pole, which one doesn't have any penguins?(2)
A. What does a microwave oven actually heat up when it cooks food?(6)

QUESTIONS 133 and 134

5 OR 6

T. What did E.T. say when he saw a kid dressed up like Yoda?(2)
R. Who is Daisy Duck's boyfriend?(1)
I. What is the name of the redheaded girl who wanted to be Superboy's girl friend?(4)
V. What attacks you in the game *Apple Panic*?(3)
I+. If you have a weight of 132 lbs. (60 kg) on Earth, and a weight of 22 lbs. (10 kg) on the moon, what is your mass?(D)
A. How many passenger pigeons are alive in the world today?(5)

QUESTIONS 133 and 134

1 OR 2

T. Atari
R. Spike
I. He runs a grocery store (Kent's General Store)
V. *Astro Chase*
I+. Diamond
A. Water (Droplets suddenly change into water vapor)

133 and 134 ANSWERS

3 OR 4

T. *Dungeons and Dragons*
R. Donald Duck
I. Krypto
V. Five
I+. The North Pole
A. Water (the moisture in the food itself)

133 and 134 ANSWERS

5 OR 6

T. "Home . . ."
R. Donald Duck
I. Lana Lang
V. Apples
I+. 132 lbs. (60 kg) (Your *mass* never changes; your *weight* varies depending on the strength of gravity)
A. None (They are extinct)

133 and 134 ANSWERS

1 OR 2

T. Including his thumb, how many fingers does E.T. have on each hand?(2)
R. Name the Three Chipmunks.(1)
I. In what city is The Batman based?(3)
V. In what kind of flying vehicle does the game *Murder on the Zinderneuf* take place?(5)
I+. What travels at approximately 300,000,000 kilometers per second?(6)
A. What dinosaur's name means "thunder lizard"?(4)

QUESTIONS 135 and 136

3 OR 4

T. What things from Earth were collected inside E.T.'s spaceship?(1)
R. Of the Three Chipmunks, who is the only one with a letter on his sweater?(3)
I. What is the name of the Police Commissioner with whom The Batman works?(4)
V. What company developed the game *Gridrunner*?(5)
I+. If you borrow $100 from the bank at 10% interest per year, how much money will you have to pay back at the end of one year?(6)
A. What does a red traffic light mean in the People's Republic of China?(2)

QUESTIONS 135 and 136

5 OR 6

T. What color were E.T.'s eyes?(1)
R. Who is the human who takes care of the Three Chipmunks?(2)
I. How does the Police Commissioner call The Batman for help?(4)
V. Complete the video game name: *Attack of the Mutant* ______.(3)
I+. Who was the first person to travel into space?(5)
A. What do the initials FM stand for in FM Radio?(6)

QUESTIONS 135 and 136

1 OR 2

T. Four
R. Simon, Theodore, and Alvin
I. Gotham City
V. Dirigible (blimp)
I+. Light
A. Brontosaurus

135 and 136 ANSWERS

3 OR 4

T. Plants and flowers
R. Alvin
I. Commissioner Gordon
V. HesWare
I+. $110
A. Go

135 and 136 ANSWERS

5 OR 6

T. Blue
R. Dave (Seville)
I. He shines the Bat Signal
V. *Camels*
I+. Yuri Gagarin
A. Frequency Modulation

135 and 136 ANSWERS

1 OR 2

T. What is the name of the movie which had the subtitle *In His Adventure on Earth*?(2)
R. Who is the only one of the Three Chipmunks to wear glasses?(1)
I. How does Superboy get into and out of his house without being seen?(3)
V. In the video game *Tron*, what is APG?(4)
I+. What would you call someone from the planet Jupiter?(5)
A. What do the initials AM stand for in AM Radio?(6)

QUESTIONS 141 and 142

3 OR 4

T. What did E.T. dress up as on Halloween?(2)
R. Which of the Three Chipmunks usually gets them all in trouble?(1)
I. Where does The Batman keep his crime-fighting equipment?(3)
V. In the video game *Tron*, what do you call the line of light left behind the light cycles?(4)
I+. What makes pasteurized milk different from regular milk?(D)
A. What traffic sign is in the shape of an octagon?(5)

QUESTIONS 141 and 142

5 OR 6

T. What kind of candies did Steven Spielberg originally want E.T. to eat?(3)
R. What cartoon mouse has two nephews called Morty and Ferdy?(2)
I. What is Robin's secret identity?(4)
V. What company produced the interactive computer game *Deadline*?(5)
I+. How many colors are there in the American flag?(1)
A. What traffic sign is in the shape of a triangle?(6)

QUESTIONS 141 and 142

1 OR 2

T. *E.T. The Extra-Terrestrial*
R. Simon
I. He has a secret tunnel (in the basement)
V. The first level of difficulty
I+. A Jovian
A. Amplitude Modulation

141 and 142 ANSWERS

3 OR 4

T. A ghost
R. Alvin
I. The Batcave
V. A light trace
I+. The milk has been heated to kill germs (or sterilized)
A. The Stop sign

141 and 142 ANSWERS

5 OR 6

T. M&Ms (He had to use Reese's Pieces instead because the first company didn't want to be linked to a "monster from space.")
R. Mickey Mouse
I. Jason Todd (Dick Grayson is now known as Nightwing)
V. Infocom
I+. Three (red, white, and blue)
A. The Yield sign

141 and 142 ANSWERS

1 OR 2

T. What did E.T. sit in when Elliot drove him around on a bicycle?(1)
R. What underwater creatures are only as big as Captain Ortega's thumb?(4)
I. What school does Superboy go to when he assumes his secret identity?(2)
V. In the game *Dungeons and Dragons*, how many sides are on the die used to roll up hit points for clerics?(6)
I+. In what city is the United Nations headquarters?(3)
A. What toy company makes Slam Shifters?(5)

QUESTIONS 143 and 144

---

3 OR 4

T. In the movie *Superman*, who did Otis work for?(4)
R. What is the name of Mickey Mouse's girl friend?(1)
I. What is the special name for The Batman's belt?(5)
V. In the *Basic Dungeons and Dragons* game, what is the highest number of experience levels to which a dwarf can advance?(D)
I+. In what country is the Sphinx?(3)
A. Where will you find Fantasyland, Adventureland, Tomorrowland, and Frontierland?(2)

QUESTIONS 143 and 144

---

5 OR 6

T. In the movie *Superman*, where was Luthor's secret headquarters?(4)
R. What is the name of the cartoon group of animals whose thoughts and feelings are spelled out on their shirts?(2)
I. What is the name of The Batman's butler?(5)
V. What is the world's most popular computer adventure game?(3)
I+. If a store is selling a $10 book at a 50% discount, how much will the book cost?(6)
A. What did Jack trade for the magic beans?(1)

QUESTIONS 143 and 144

1 OR 2

T. A carrier basket
R. Snorks
I. Smallville High
V. Six
I+. New York
A. Kenner

143 and 144 ANSWERS

3 OR 4

T. Lex Luthor
R. Minnie Mouse
I. The Bat Utility Belt
V. Twelve
I+. Egypt
A. Disneyland and/or The Magic Kingdom in Walt Disney World

143 and 144 ANSWERS

5 OR 6

T. Underground (beneath Metropolis)
R. The Shirt Tales
I. Alfred
V. *Zork I*
I+. $5
A. His cow

143 and 144 ANSWERS

1 OR 2

T. What did the man who was trying to catch E.T. wear on his belt?(4)
R. What TV starship is under the command of the United Federation of Planets?(1)
I. On what color background is the bat symbol on the chest of The Batman's costume?(3)
V. What was the first commercially produced war game?(D)
I+. In what country do the people of Rhode Island live?(2)
A. How many keys are there on a piano?(5)

QUESTIONS 145 and 146

3 OR 4

T. In *E.T.*, how many sisters did Elliot have?(1)
R. What is the name of Mickey Mouse's dog?(2)
I. What is the special name of The Batman's boomerang?(5)
V. What must you do in the Colecovision game *War Room*?(4)
I+. What was the name of the American space station that crashed back to Earth?(6)
A. Which comic-book company publishes the adventures of Thor and Iron Man?(3)

QUESTIONS 145 and 146

5 OR 6

T. What do the letters E.T. stand for?(5)
R. What kind of an animal is Scooby-Doo?(1)
I. What color is Robin's cape?(4)
V. In the hand game, if scissors cut paper, what does paper wrap?(2)
I+. How many colors are in the Canadian flag?(6)
A. What do you call the person who leads an orchestra?(3)

QUESTIONS 145 and 146

1 OR 2

T. Keys
R. U.S.S. *Enterprise*
I. Yellow
V. *Tactics II*
I+. United States
A. Eighty-eight

145 and 146 ANSWERS

3 OR 4

T. One
R. Pluto
I. The Batarang
V. Defend the United States from a nuclear attack
I+. Skylab
A. Marvel

145 and 146 ANSWERS

5 OR 6

T. Extra Terrestrial (Okay, okay, they can also stand for the TV show *Entertainment Tonight*)
R. A dog
I. Yellow
V. Stone
I+. Two (red and white)
A. A conductor

145 and 146 ANSWERS

1 OR 2

T. In the first *King Kong* movie, what building did Kong climb?(2)
R. What kind of hat does Donald Duck wear?(4)
I. What color are Robin's gloves?(5)
V. What is the subtitle for the second video game about Frogger?(6)
I+. If it costs $2.50 for one ticket to see a movie, how much will two tickets cost?(1)
A. What is the body of the Corvette car made from?(3)

QUESTIONS 151 and 152

---

3 OR 4

T. What were Elliot and E.T. doing when E.T. made them fly?(1)
R. Which cartoon bird has two nephews named Splinter and Topknot?(5)
I. What color is The Batman's belt?(2)
V. In what game do you call out the map coordinates you want to "bomb," so you can sink your opponent's warships?(3)
I+. What has a positive and negative terminal?(6)
A. Where do the Care Bears live?(4)

QUESTIONS 151 and 152

---

5 OR 6

T. What toy did E.T. use to make his radio?(4)
R. In what year was Moonbase Alpha blasted from its orbit around the Earth?(3)
I. If you were standing in front of Robin, on which side of his costume would you see the letter R?(2)
V. From what two vehicles did the game *Sub-Roc* get its name?(5)
I+. How many minutes are in three-quarters of an hour?(1)
A. How many ghosts "live" in Walt Disney's Haunted Mansion?(6)

QUESTIONS 151 and 152

1 OR 2

T. The Empire State Building
R. A sailor's hat
I. Green
V. *Threedeep*
I+. $5
A. Fiberglas

151 and 152 ANSWERS

---

3 OR 4

T. Riding bicycle
R. Woody Woodpecker
I. Yellow
V. *Battleship*
I+. A battery
A. Care-A-Lot

151 and 152 ANSWERS

---

5 OR 6

T. A Speak and Spell
R. 1999
I. Right
V. *Sub*marine and *roc*ket
I+. Forty-five
A. 999

151 and 152 ANSWERS

1 OR 2

T. What is another name for the planet Arrakis?(6)
R. In what city do the Flintstones live?(1)
I. What disability does Daredevil have?(4)
V. Complete the name of the video game designed by Rob Fulop: *Demon* ______.(2)
I+. How many days in two weeks?(3)
A. On what series of books would you find the author name Franklin W. Dixon?(5)

QUESTIONS 153 and 154

3 OR 4

T. Name two parts of E.T.'s body that glowed.(2)
R. What is the name of Wilma Flintstone's husband?(1)
I. What color is Daredevil's costume?(4)
V. In Scott Adams's *The Count*, what happens when you smoke in the crypt?(D)
I+. How often does a leap year usually come?(5)
A. What is the name of the vitamins that are shaped like cartoon characters from the Stone Age?(3)

QUESTIONS 153 and 154

5 OR 6

T. What kind of toys did Elliot first show to E.T.?(3)
R. What is the name of Barney Rubble's wife?(2)
I. When he assumes his secret identity, what does Daredevil do for a living?(5)
V. When two people play *Joust*, who is their opponent?(4)
I+. Why is a computer keyboard usually called a QWERTY keyboard?(6)
A. What country did tacos first come from?(1)

QUESTIONS 153 and 154

1 OR 2

T. Dune
R. Bedrock
I. He is blind
V. *Attack*
I+. Fourteen
A. *The Hardy Boys*

153 and 154 ANSWERS

3 OR 4

T. His finger and his chest (or his heart)
R. Fred Flintstone
I. Red
V. "There is a coffin' in the room."
I+. Every four years (To be a leap year, the year must be divisible by 4. However, if the year is a "century" year like 1900 or 2000, it has to be divisible by 400. So every couple of hundred years, it takes eight years for a leap year to come up.)
A. Flintstones (multivitamins)

153 and 154 ANSWERS

5 OR 6

T. *Star Wars* Action Figures
R. Betty Rubble
I. He is a lawyer
V. The machine
I+. That is the order of the first six letters in the top row of letter keys
A. Mexico

153 and 154 ANSWERS

1 OR 2

T. What did E.T. drink that made him drunk?(2)
R. What is the name of the Flintstones' daughter?(3)
I. What is the name of Richie Rich's robot maid?(6)
V. In poker, does a full house beat four of a kind?(4)
I+. What part of a plant is a potato?(1)
A. In the book *The Secret Garden*, where was Mary born?(5)

QUESTIONS 155 and 156

3 OR 4

T. Which *Jaws* movie was first made in 3-D?(1)
R. What is the name of the Flintstones' pet dinosaur?(5)
I. What is the name of the spoiled rich kid who is always trying to give Richie Rich a hard time?(6)
V. What do you roll with two dice when you roll snake eyes?(4)
I+. What fruit do raisins come from?(3)
A. Would you need a ladder or a shovel to gather peanuts?(2)

QUESTIONS 155 and 156

5 OR 6

T. What did E.T. do when Elliot threw a ball into the shed?(4)
R. What is the name of the Rubbles' son?(1)
I. What color is Richie Rich's hair?(3)
V. What do you roll with two dice when you roll boxcars?(6)
I+. What vegetable do pickles come from?(5)
A. In a bunch of what kind of fruit might you find a tarantula?(2)

QUESTIONS 155 and 156

1 OR 2

T. Beer
R. Pebbles
I. Irona
V. No
I+. A root
A. India

155 and 156 ANSWERS

---

3 OR 4

T. *Jaws 3-D*
R. Dingo
I. Reggie Van Dough
V. One and one
I+. Grapes
A. A shovel (Peanuts grow underground)

155 and 156 ANSWERS

---

5 OR 6

T. Threw it back
R. Bamm Bamm
I. Yellow (or blonde)
V. Six and six
I+. Cucumbers
A. Bananas

155 and 156 ANSWERS

1 OR 2

T. What did Luke Skywalker destroy in *Star Wars* that Darth Vader tried to build again in *Return of the Jedi*?(3)
R. Who does Wile E. Coyote always try to catch?(1)
I. What kind of clothes does Hot Stuff wear?(5)
V. In *Joust*, what does an enemy bird do each time you unseat its rider?(2)
I+. Off which country's coastline would you find the Great Barrier Reef?(4)
A. What is a baby owl called?(6)

QUESTIONS 161 and 162

3 OR 4

T. In what movie did Davey Osborne have an imaginary play-mate named Jack Flack?(4)
R. What is the Roadrunner's name?(2)
I. What does Hot Stuff always carry?(5)
V. What company first developed the arcade version of *Joust*?(6)
I+. What country does the duck-billed platypus come from?(1)
A. Who did Dr. Jekyll turn into when he drank his special potion?(3)

QUESTIONS 161 and 162

5 OR 6

T. In *Return of the Jedi*, what was Artoo doing during the party on Jabba's flying boat?(4)
R. Where does Wile E. Coyote get all of the things he needs to make his traps?(6)
I. What does Hot Stuff have on his head that regular people don't?(2)
V. What company developed the *Star Wars* arcade game?(5)
I+. What country do kangaroos come from?(1)
A. How many horns did the triceratops dinosaur have?(3)

QUESTIONS 161 and 162

1 OR 2

T. The Death Star
R. The Roadrunner
I. Diapers
V. It drops an egg
I+. Australia
A. An owlet

161 and 162 ANSWERS

3 OR 4

T. *Cloak and Dagger*
R. Beep Beep
I. A pitchfork (or trident)
V. William's
I+. Australia
A. Mr. Hyde

161 and 162 ANSWERS

5 OR 6

T. He was serving drinks
R. From the ACME company
I. Horns
V. Atari
I+. Australia
A. Three

161 and 162 ANSWERS

1 OR 2

T. What was the name of the animal Luke Skywalker rode on the frozen world of Hoth?(3)
R. Who is the only Smurf to wear red pants and a red hat?(1)
I. How did Spider-man get his superpowers?(2)
V. What is the goal of the *Star Wars* arcade game?(5)
I+. What is the highest elected office in Canada?(6)
A. What do you look at to tell the difference between an Indian and an African elephant?(4)

QUESTIONS 163 and 164

3 OR 4

T. In *The Empire Strikes Back*, did the giant walking machines belong to the Rebels or to the Empire?(4)
R. What is the name of the only girl Smurf?(2)
I. What is Spider-man's secret identity?(5)
V. What do you fly in the arcade *Star Wars* game?(6)
I+. What is the highest elected office in the United States?(1)
A. Is a zebra a white animal with black stripes or a black animal with white stripes?(3)

QUESTIONS 163 and 164

5 OR 6

T. In *The Empire Strikes Back*, who did Luke Skywalker meet on the jungle world of Degobah?(3)
R. Whose village is the evil Gargamel always trying to destroy?(1)
I. Which newspaper does Peter Parker work for?(5)
V. Complete the Atari video game name: *Crystal* ______.(4)
I+. What is the highest elected office in England?(6)
A. How can you tell the age of a tree?(2)

QUESTIONS 163 and 164

1 OR 2

T. A taun-taun
R. Poppa Smurf
I. He was bitten by a radioactive spider
V. To destroy the Death Star
I+. Prime Minister
A. The elephants' ears (African elephants have larger ears)

163 and 164 ANSWERS

3 OR 4

T. The Empire
R. Smurfette
I. Peter Parker
V. An X-Wing Fighter
I+. President
A. A black animal with white stripes

163 and 164 ANSWERS

5 OR 6

T. Yoda
R. The Smurfs'
I. *The Daily Bugle*
V. *Castles*
I+. Prime Minister
A. Count its growth rings

163 and 164 ANSWERS

1 OR 2

T. In what movie would you find the Tin Man and Cowardly Lion?(1)
R. Which Smurf has a tattoo of a heart on his shoulder?(2)
I. In which comic book will you find newspaper Publisher J. Jonah Jameson?(4)
V. What is the name of the player character in *Crystal Castles*?(3)
I+. How many months are in three years?(6)
A. In Roman mythology, who was Hercules' father?(5)

QUESTIONS 165 and 166

3 OR 4

T. In *The Wizard of Oz*, where was the first place Dorothy landed?(1)
R. Which Smurf wears glasses?(3)
I. What is the name of Spider-man's aunt?(2)
V. Which computer game company publishes a newsletter called the *New Zork Times*?(6)
I+. How many weeks are in one year?(5)
A. In what country would you break a pinata at Christmas time?(4)

QUESTIONS 165 and 166

5 OR 6

T. In *The Wizard of Oz*, what did the Scarecrow want from the Wizard?(3)
R. What does the Smurf called Vanity always carry?(2)
I. What superhero is nicknamed "the ol' webslinger"?(1)
V. What kind of game do the Sargon computer programs play?(5)
I+. How many seasons a year are there in North America?(4)
A. What was Doctor Frankenstein's first name?(6)

QUESTIONS 165 and 166

1 OR 2

T. *The Wizard of Oz*
R. Hefty
I. *The Amazing Spider-man*
V. Bentley Bear
I+. Thirty-six
A. Zeus

165 and 166 ANSWERS

3 OR 4

T. Munchkin Land
R. Brainy
I. Aunt May
V. Infocom
I+. Fifty-two
A. Mexico

165 and 166 ANSWERS

5 OR 6

T. A brain
R. A mirror
I. Spider-man
V. Chess
I+. Four
A. Victor

165 and 166 ANSWERS

1 OR 2

T. In *The Wizard of Oz*, what did Dorothy throw on the Wicked Witch of the West to make her melt?(1)
R. On *The Smurfs*, what kind of an animal is Azrael?(4)
I. What is the name of Richie Rich's dog?(5)
V. What company developed the game *Dragon's Lair*?(3)
I+. Name the three countries in North America.(6)
A. What do you get if you catch a leprechaun?(2)

QUESTIONS 211 and 212

3 OR 4

T. In *The Wizard of Oz*, what was the name of Dorothy's dog?(3)
R. Which Smurf likes to play jokes?(1)
I. What is the name of Richie Rich's nurse?(5)
V. What do the initials BMX stand for?(6)
I+. In what ocean do you find Hawaii?(4)
A. What is supposedly found at the end of the rainbow?(2)

QUESTIONS 211 and 212

5 OR 6

T. In *The Wizard of Oz*, what city did the Wizard live in?(4)
R. Which Smurf likes to make music?(3)
I. What does Wendy the Good Little Witch ride on?(1)
V. What is the name of the vector-graphic Atari tank-battle game that was adapted to train American soldiers?(5)
I+. Name the two oceans that touch the United States.(2)
A. In what modern-day country would you find what was once the old country of Transylvania?(D)

QUESTIONS 211 and 212

1 OR 2

T. Water
R. A cat
I. Dollar
V. Cinematronics
I+. Canada, the United States, and Mexico
A. The leprechaun's gold

211 and 212 ANSWERS

---

3 OR 4

T. Toto
R. Jokey
I. Nurse Jenny
V. Bicycle Motocross
I+. The Pacific
A. A pot of gold

211 and 212 ANSWERS

---

5 OR 6

T. The Emerald City
R. Harmony
I. A broom
V. *Battlezone*
I+. Atlantic and Pacific
A. Rumania

211 and 212 ANSWERS

1 OR 2

T. In *The Wizard of Oz*, what state did Dorothy come from?(6)
R. What blue creatures are only three apples high?(3)
I. Which superhero uses a magical golden lasso?(2)
V. What was the first video game to become such a hit that there was actually a shortage of quarters in some parts of the United States?(5)
I+. In what country do the people of Madrid live?(4)
A. What supernatural creature do you supposedly kill by driving a stake through its heart?(1)

QUESTIONS 213 and 214

3 OR 4

T. In *The Wizard of Oz*, what did the Cowardly Lion want from the Wizard?(4)
R. What were the little fighter spaceships in *Battlestar Galactica* called?(6)
I. What symbol is on Wonder Woman's headband?(5)
V. Before there were trivia games, what was the number-one all-time favorite board game?(3)
I+. In what country do the people of Los Angeles live?(1)
A. What supernatural creature supposedly can be killed only by a silver bullet?(2)

QUESTIONS 213 and 214

5 OR 6

T. In *The Wizard of Oz*, what kind of road did Dorothy have to follow?(1)
R. What spaceship was Commander Adama in charge of?(2)
I. Which superhero has a friend named Etta Candy?(4)
V. Which brand of home computer uses player-missiles in games?(5)
I+. In what country do the people of Beijing live?(6)
A. What plant can't a vampire stand?(3)

QUESTIONS 213 and 214

1 OR 2

T. Kansas
R. Smurfs
I. Wonder Woman
V. *Space Invaders*
I+. Spain
A. A vampire

213 and 214 ANSWERS

3 OR 4

T. Courage
R. Vipers
I. A star
V. *Monopoly*
I+. The United States
A. A werewolf

213 and 214 ANSWERS

5 OR 6

T. The yellow brick road
R. Battlestar *Galactica*
I. Wonder Woman
V. Atari
I+. China (The People's Republic of)
A. Garlic (The mustard plant is also said to annoy vampires because they supposedly have to stop and count all the seeds)

213 and 214 ANSWERS

1 OR 2

T. In *The Wizard of Oz*, what was the name of Dorothy's aunt?(4)
R. In *Battlestar Galactica*, what was the name of the evil silver aliens?(1)
I. What superhero's real name is Ben Grimm?(2)
V. What is the name of the hand-held game that plays *Scrabble*?(6)
I+. Name one of the two longest rivers in the world.(5)
A. How many brains did the stegosaur dinosaur have?(3)

QUESTIONS 215 and 216

3 OR 4

T. In *The Wizard of Oz*, what kind of flying animals did the Wicked Witch of the West send to attack Dorothy?(2)
R. In *Battlestar Galactica*, what planet were the humans trying to find?(1)
I. What superhero's real name is Johnny Storm?(4)
V. What company developed the game *Jupiter Lander* for its own line of computers?(3)
I+. What is the smallest continent?(5)
A. Who said "Baby in my drink" and why was this important?(6)

QUESTIONS 215 and 216

5 OR 6

T. In *The Wizard of Oz*, what did Dorothy have to tap together when she wanted to go home?(4)
R. In *Battlestar Galactica*, what kind of warriors were the fighter spaceship pilots?(1)
I. What superhero's real name is Susan Richards?(3)
V. What is the setting of the Avalon Hill computer game, *Thank Goodness It's Friday*?(5)
I+. In which country is the world's highest waterfall: Venezuela, South Africa, or New Zealand?(6)
A. What do you call a three-dimensional photograph taken with laser light?(2)

QUESTIONS 215 and 216

1 OR 2

T. Auntie Em
R. Cylons
I. The Thing
V. *Monty Plays Scrabble*
I+. The Nile or the Amazon (People are still arguing which is longer)
A. Two

215 and 216 ANSWERS

---

3 OR 4

T. Flying monkeys
R. Earth
I. The Human Torch
V. Commodore
I+. Australia
A. Washoe the chimpanzee said this sentence in sign language after she dropped a doll in her glass; this is important because it was the first complete sentence spoken by a non-human

215 and 216 ANSWERS

---

5 OR 6

T. The red shoes
R. Colonial Warriors
I. The Invisible Girl
V. An office party
I+. Venezuela (Angel Falls)
A. A hologram

215 and 216 ANSWERS

1 OR 2

T. In what movie did a space monster kill all but one crew member of the spaceship *Nostromo*?(1)
R. In *Battlestar Galactica*, did Baltaar work for the humans or the aliens?(2)
I. What superhero's real name is Dr. Reed Richards?(5)
V. What should you wear on your feet to compete in the slalom?(4)
I+. What is the name of the canal that joins the Atlantic and the Pacific oceans?(3)
A. Which major American city was once called New Amsterdam?(6)

QUESTIONS 221

3 OR 4

T. What kind of animal survived at the end of the movie *Alien*?(1)
R. In *Battlestar Galactica*, what was the name of the robot who worked for Baltaar?(6)
I. What superhero's real name is Donald Blake?(4)
V. What is the highest trophy in the NHL?(3)
I+. Is Washington, D.C., closer to the state of New York or the state of California?(2)
A. Which state is known as the Lone Star State?(5)

QUESTIONS 221

5 OR 6

T. What did the surviving member do to the big spaceship at the end of *Alien*?(2)
R. In *Battlestar Galactica*, what was the name of the little boy?(3)
I. What superhero's real name is Steve Rogers?(5)
V. Which hockey player wears number 99?(1)
I+. Name two of the three particles that make up an atom.(6)
A. Which car company makes the Golf?(4)

QUESTIONS 221

1 OR 2

T. *Alien*
R. The aliens
I. Mr. Fantastic
V. Skis
I+. The Panama Canal
A. New York

221 ANSWERS

---

3 OR 4

T. A cat
R. Lucifer
I. The Mighty Thor
V. The Stanley Cup
I+. New York
A. Texas

221 ANSWERS

---

5 OR 6

T. She blew it up
R. Boxey
I. Captain America
V. Wayne Gretzky
I+. Protons, neutrons, or electrons
A. Volkswagen

221 ANSWERS

1 OR 2

T. At the end of the movie *Monty Python and the Holy Grail*, what kind of animal killed most of the knights?(1)
R. In *Battlestar Galactica*, what was the name of the robot dog?(3)
I. What superhero's real name is Barry Allen?(4)
V. What video-game company developed *River Raid*?(5)
I+. In which country would you use yen as money?(2)
A. What is the name of E.T.'s spaceship?(D)

QUESTIONS 222

3 OR 4

T. In *Mickey's Christmas Carol*, who played the part of Ebenezer Scrooge?(1)
R. In *Battlestar Galactica*, what was the word for "years"?(5)
I. What superhero's real name is Oliver Queen?(6)
V. What happens after the very last screen of the arcade version of *Donkey Kong*?(3)
I+. How many notes are in a regular musical scale?(4)
A. Who talked with a Pushmepullyu?(2)

QUESTIONS 222

5 OR 6

T. What was the title of the Monty Python movie in which a man ate so much he exploded?(4)
R. In *Battlestar Galactica*, who could fly the fighter spaceships: just men, just women, or both men and women?(2)
I. What superhero's real name is Linda Lee Danvers?(1)
V. What is your final target in the video game *Zaxxon*?(5)
I+. In what city would you find Big Ben?(3)
A. Who wrote *Tom Sawyer* and *Huckleberry Finn*?(6)

QUESTIONS 222

1 OR 2

T. A rabbit
R. Muffit
I. Flash
V. Activision
I+. Japan
A. *The Grand Ornament (Jewel of the Galaxy)*

222 ANSWERS

3 OR 4

T. Uncle Scrooge McDuck
R. Yarns
I. Green Arrow
V. The man and woman get together and a heart forms over their heads
I+. Eight
A. Doctor Doolittle

222 ANSWERS

5 OR 6

T. *The Meaning of Life*
R. Men and women
I. Supergirl
V. The Zaxxon Robot
I+. London
A. Mark Twain

222 ANSWERS

1 OR 2

T. What sport was featured in the *Rocky* movies?(1)
R. What animated superhero wears a red costume, dark glasses, and can stretch himself into different shapes?(4)
I. What superpower does The Batman have?(3)
V. What kind of animals must you defend from the wolves in the video game *Pooyan*?(5)
I+. In what country would you find the Eiffel Tower?(2)
A. What kind of a scientist was E.T.?(6)

QUESTIONS 223 and 224

---

3 OR 4

T. In *Flashdance*, what was the girl's regular job?(2)
R. In *B.J. and the Bear*, what kind of animal was Bear?(1)
I. What superpower does Flash have?(4)
V. What two game elements are present in "hybrid" video games?(6)
I+. In what city would you find the Empire State Building?(3)
A. Name the part of the Macintosh computer that you roll around on a table in order to point to something on the screen.(5)

QUESTIONS 223 and 224

---

5 OR 6

T. Whose lightsaber did Obi-wan give to Luke Skywalker in *Star Wars*?(2)
R. In *B.J. and the Bear*, what did B.J. drive?(1)
I. What superpower does Quicksilver have?(3)
V. What is the name of your opponent in the *Discs of Tron*?(5)
I+. In what city would you find the CN Tower?(6)
A. What comic-book company publishes *Flash* and *Green Lantern*?(4)

QUESTIONS 223 and 224

1 OR 2

T. Boxing
R. Plastic Man
I. None
V. Piglets
I+. France
A. A botanist (He studied plants)

223 and 224 ANSWERS

3 OR 4

T. She was a welder
R. A chimpanzee
I. Superspeed
V. A board-game section and a computer-game section
I+. New York
A. Mouse

223 and 224 ANSWERS

5 OR 6

T. Luke Skywalker's father's
R. A truck
I. Superspeed
V. Sark
I+. Toronto
A. D.C.

223 and 224 ANSWERS

1 OR 2

T. What TV series starred the actor who played Khan in the *Star Trek* movie *The Wrath of Khan*?(3)
R. In what country was the series *Dr. Who* made?(1)
I. What supergroup does the Human Torch belong to?(2)
V. How many people are needed to play the card game Bridge?(4)
I+. What is the capital of Canada?(6)
A. What is the magazine *Starlog* about?(5)

QUESTIONS 225 and 226

3 OR 4

T. What happened to Mr. Spock at the end of the *Star Trek* movie *The Wrath of Khan*?(1)
R. What was the name of Dr. Who's robot dog?(4)
I. What supergroup does Iron Man belong to?(5)
V. What are the two basic game options in the laser arcade game *MACH 3*?(6)
I+. In what country would you find the Leaning Tower of Pisa?(2)
A. What safety warning is on the side of a McDonald's Cherry Pie?(3)

QUESTIONS 225 and 226

5 OR 6

T. In the *Star Trek* movie *The Wrath of Khan*, what was the name of the device that exploded and created the new planet?(3)
R. What did Dr. Who's TARDIS look like from the outside?(1)
I. What supergroup does Hawkman belong to?(4)
V. What is the name of the arcade car-race game that has three video screens for a wraparound view?(5)
I+. Which artist painted the Mona Lisa?(6)
A. What do you call the toy that looks like a long floppy spring and can walk downstairs by itself?(2)

QUESTIONS 225 and 226

1 OR 2

T. *Fantasy Island* (Ricardo Montalban was the actor's name)
R. England
I. Fantastic Four
V. Four
I+. Ottawa
A. Science-fiction movies and television

225 and 226 ANSWERS

3 OR 4

T. He died
R. K-9
I. Avengers
V. Bomber option or Fighter option
I+. Italy
A. "Caution: Filling is hot"

225 and 226 ANSWERS

5 OR 6

T. Genesis Device
R. A British police call box (or a blue phone booth)
I. The Justice League of America
V. *TX-1*
I+. Leonardo da Vinci
A. Slinky

225 and 226 ANSWERS

1 OR 2

T. Who was the hero of *Raiders of the Lost Ark*?(1)
R. What was the name of the little robot on *Buck Rogers*?(2)
I. Which superhero lives in Chicago and goes to Lake Shore University?(6)
V. Who is the star of the laser arcade game *Cliff Hanger*?(4)
I·. Beginning with "Do, re," what are the notes in a musical scale?(5)
A. What city does Godzilla like to have for dinner?(3)

QUESTIONS 231 and 232

3 OR 4

T. What was wriggling in the pit that Bellocq threw Indiana Jones and Marian Ravenwood into?(1)
R. Who was Lieutenant Wilma Deering's sometime boy-friend, sometimes?(4)
I. What color is Supergirl's hair?(2)
V. Who tries to bash you in *Quest for Tires*?(5)
I·. How many eggs are in two-and-a-half dozen?(3)
A. In what would you find a tweeter and a woofer?(6)

QUESTIONS 231 and 232

5 OR 6

T. What was the name of the Ark in *Raiders of the Lost Ark*?(4)
R. On which TV show would you see the characters Dr. Huer and Dr. Theophilus?(3)
I. What group of superheroes is led by Professor X?(1)
V. What company developed the arcade version of *Dig Dug*?(5)
I·. The first ordinary person to ride the space shuttle will be what kind of teacher?(2)
A. In what kind of household machine would you find a bob-bin?(6)

QUESTIONS 231 and 232

1 OR 2

T. Indiana Jones
R. Twiki
I. Supergirl
V. Cliff
I+. Do, re, mi, fa, so, la, ti, do
A. Tokyo

231 and 232 ANSWERS

3 OR 4

T. Snakes
R. Buck Rogers
I. Blonde
V. The Fat Broad
I+. Thirty
A. A stereo speaker

231 and 232 ANSWERS

5 OR 6

T. The Ark of the Covenant
R. *Buck Rogers*
I. The X-Men
V. Atari
I+. A science teacher
A. A sewing machine

231 and 232 ANSWERS

1 OR 2

T. How did Indiana Jones stop the man with the sword in the marketplace?(1)
R. What was the name of the character on *Buck Rogers* who had feathers instead of hair?(6)
I. What kind of person must you be to join the X-Men?(5)
V. In what video game are you digging for Pookas and Frygars?(3)
I+. What four-footed mammal can't move all four feet off the ground at once?(4)
A. What kind of an animal was Moby Dick?(2)

QUESTIONS 233 and 234

3 OR 4

T. What was Indiana Jones good at cracking?(2)
R. In what century does *Buck Rogers* take place?(5)
I. What happens when the X-Man Cyclops takes off his glasses?(6)
V. What are cats'-eyes, steelies, and boulders?(3)
I+. What underwater creature has five arms and can grow them back if they are broken off?(4)
A. What ran up the clock in the poem "Hickory Dickory Dock"?(1)

QUESTIONS 233 and 234

5 OR 6

T. What happens to the Ark at the end of *Raiders of the Lost Ark*?(6)
R. What is the name of the dog in *The Get Along Gang*?(2)
I. In *The X-Men*, what kind of a creature does Lockheed look like?(5)
V. What is the name of the gigantic computer adventure game from Sierra that contains more than 1,300 rooms?(4)
I+. Where do pearls generally come from?(1)
A. What did Peter Piper pick?(3)

QUESTIONS 233 and 234

1 OR 2

T. He shot him
R. Hawk
I. A mutant
V. *Dig Dug*
I+. An elephant
A. A (great white) whale

233 and 234 ANSWERS

3 OR 4

T. His whip
R. The twenty-fifth century
I. Force beams shoot from his eyes
V. Marbles
I+. A starfish
A. A mouse

233 and 234 ANSWERS

5 OR 6

T. It is put away in a warehouse
R. Dotty
I. A dragon
V. *Time Zone*
I+. Oysters
A. A peck of pickled peppers

233 and 234 ANSWERS

1 OR 2

T. In *Star Wars*, where were Obi-wan and Darth Vader when they had their final fight?(1)
R. On TV, how long was the starship *Enterprise*'s mission?(6)
I. What supergroup does the Scarlet Witch belong to?(5)
V. Which aliens do you blast out of space in the video game *Star Trek*?(2)
I+. Is a persimmon a monkey or a fruit?(3)
A. What did she sell by the sea shore?(4)

QUESTIONS 235 and 236

3 OR 4

T. In *Star Wars*, who sold Artoo and Threepio to Luke?(3)
R. On *Star Trek*, what was the name of the device that "beamed" people from the *Enterprise* to the ground?(2)
I. What supergroup does Starfox belong to?(6)
V. What company developed the arcade game based on the movie *Firefox*?(4)
I+. What do you call the place where coins are made and paper money is printed?(5)
A. What did Horton hear?(1)

QUESTIONS 235 and 236

5 OR 6

T. In *Star Wars*, what were Luke and Han disguised as when they went to rescue Leia?(4)
R. On *Star Trek*, what were the crew's ray guns called?(2)
I. What supergroup does the Vision belong to?(6)
V. In what sport does a goalie stand in the crease?(1)
I+. How many centimeters in a meter?(3)
A. What kind of trap did Piglet fall into?(5)

QUESTIONS 235 and 236

1 OR 2

T. In the Death Star
R. Five years
I. The Avengers
V. Klingons
I+. A fruit
A. Sea shells

235 and 236 ANSWERS

3 OR 4

T. The Jawas
R. The Transporter
I. The Avengers
V. Atari
I+. The mint
A. A Who

235 and 236 ANSWERS

5 OR 6

T. Imperial Stormtroopers
R. Phasers
I. The Avengers
V. Hockey
I+. One hundred
A. A heffalump trap

235 and 236 ANSWERS

1 OR 2

T. In the movie *Alien*, one crew member wasn't human. What was he?(2)
R. In what city did Buck Rogers live when he returned to Earth?(6)
I. Where is the Justice League of America's headquarters?(1)
V. In what sport are there hazards, fairways, and traps?(5)
I+. What kind of snake spreads the skin around its head to warn that it may strike?(3)
A. Who is Baby Roo's mother?(4)

QUESTIONS 241 and 242

3 OR 4

T. In the movie *Rocky*, what kind of a store did Rocky's girl friend work in?(3)
R. What kind of a Lord was Dr. Who?(4)
I. What can the superhero Atom do?(1)
V. Which end of a bat does a baseball player swing at the ball: the meat end or the knob end?(2)
I+. Is a horned toad a toad or a lizard?(5)
A. What does FBI stand for?(6)

QUESTIONS 241 and 242

5 OR 6

T. In *Superman III*, what comedian played the computer expert?(1)
R. In *Star Trek*, what planet did Mr. Spock come from?(3)
I. Which member of the Justice League of America can stretch?(5)
V. On a hockey rink, what color is the center line?(2)
I+. What's a shorter way of saying "light amplification by stimulated emission of radiation"?(6)
A. What's a shorter name for the United Nations International Children's Emergency Fund?(4)

QUESTIONS 241 and 242

1 OR 2

T. A robot
R. New Chicago
I. In orbit
V. Golf
I+. A cobra
A. Kanga

241 and 242 ANSWERS

---

3 OR 4

T. A pet store
R. A Time Lord
I. Shrink
V. The meat end
I+. A lizard
A. Federal Bureau of Investigation

241 and 242 ANSWERS

---

5 OR 6

T. Richard Pryor
R. Vulcan
I. The Elongated Man
V. Red
I+. Laser
A. UNICEF

241 and 242 ANSWERS

1 OR 2

T. In the *Star Trek* movie *The Wrath of Khan*, what was James Kirk's rank?(2)
R. Who says "Nyaah, what's up, doc?"(1)
I. What color is Batgirl's hair?(4)
V. In hockey, what part of the rink lies between the two blue lines?(6)
I+. At the end of a letter, what do the letters P.S. stand for?(5)
A. What do the letters V.I.P. stand for?(3)

QUESTIONS 243 and 244

---

3 OR 4

T. In the *Star Trek* movie *The Wrath of Khan*, what kind of alien was Lieutenant Saavik?(D)
R. What is the name of the little man with the big red mustache who is always chasing after Bugs Bunny?(3)
I. By what name is J'onn J'onzz known to the public when he comes to Earth?(4)
V. What are the colors on a soccer ball?(1)
I+. Which American state was purchased from the Russians for $7.2 million?(5)
A. How many are in a trio?(2)

QUESTIONS 243 and 244

---

5 OR 6

T. In the *Star Trek* movie *The Wrath of Khan*, what did Kirk find he had that he never knew about?(6)
R. What is the name of the cat that always chases Tweety Pie?(2)
I. What supergroup does Wonder Woman belong to?(3)
V. What piece of equipment is used in rebound tumbling?(5)
I+. If your thumb is number one, and your little finger is number five, what number is your index finger?(4)
A. How many are in a duo?(1)

QUESTIONS 243 and 244

1 OR 2

T. Admiral
R. Bugs Bunny
I. Red
V. The neutral zone
I+. Post Script (a note added at the end of a letter)
A. Very Important Person

243 and 244 ANSWERS

---

3 OR 4

T. He was half Vulcan and half Romulan
R. Yosemite Sam (pronounced *Yo*-SEM-*ih-tee*)
I. The Martian Manhunter
V. Black and white
I+. Alaska
A. Three

243 and 244 ANSWERS

---

5 OR 6

T. A son
R. Sylvester
I. The Justice League of America
V. A trampoline
I+. Two
A. Two

243 and 244 ANSWERS

1 OR 2

T. What was the title of the movie that featured six dwarfs called Randall, Fidgit, Wally, Og, Strutter, and Vermin?(6)
R. What is the TV show *Hill Street Blues* about?(2)
I. Of Archie's two girl friends, which one has blonde hair?(5)
V. What kind of golf club is usually used to hit a ball from a tee?(4)
I+. Name the three primary colors.(3)
A. How many in a pair?(1)

QUESTIONS 245 and 246

3 OR 4

T. What happened to Kevin's house at the end of *Time Bandits*?(6)
R. Who was the host of *The Muppet Show*?(1)
I. What is Archie's last name?(5)
V. What kind of golf club is generally used to hit a ball on the green?(3)
I+. Which two colors, when mixed, make green?(4)
A. How many actors are used to perform a monologue?(2)

QUESTIONS 245 and 246

5 OR 6

T. In the movie *Time Bandits*, what kind of map did the dwarfs steal?(6)
R. What was the name of the bear on *The Muppet Show*?(1)
I. What is the name of Archie's school?(2)
V. What is the name of the plastic disk, used for throwing, that was developed from a pie plate?(5)
I+. Which two colors, when mixed, make purple?(3)
A. How many are in a dozen?(4)

QUESTIONS 245 and 246

1 OR 2

T. *Time Bandits* (If you listen to the movie carefully, you'll learn that there was a seventh dwarf named Horseflesh, but he died before the story began)
R. Police officers (and other people at their station)
I. Betty
V. A wood
I+. Red, yellow, and blue
A. Two

245 and 246 ANSWERS

3 OR 4

T. It exploded and burned
R. Kermit the Frog
I. Andrews
V. A putter
I+. Yellow and blue
A. One

245 and 246 ANSWERS

5 OR 6

T. A map of the Universe (showing all the holes in Time)
R. Fozzie
I. Riverdale High
V. Frisbee
I+. Red and blue
A. Twelve

245 and 246 ANSWERS

1 OR 2

T. What was the name of the barbarian warrior played by Arnold Schwarzenegger in two movies?(1)
R. On *The Muppet Show*, what was the name of the muppet who wanted Kermit to be her boyfriend?(2)
I. Who does Reggie call "ol' carrot top"?(4)
V. What company makes the official Frisbee?(5)
I+. Which two colors, when mixed, make orange?(3)
A. How many are in a gross?(D)

QUESTIONS 251 and 252

3 OR 4

T. What was the name of the actor who played Han Solo *and* Indiana Jones?(1)
R. On *The Muppet Show*, what was the name of Dr. Bunsen Honeydew's assistant at Muppet Labs?(3)
I. Who is the principal of Archie's school?(2)
V. Where is the "sweet spot" on a tennis racket?(4)
I+. If you had a unicycle, a tricycle, and a bicycle, how many wheels would you have altogether?(5)
A. How many are in a baker's dozen?(6)

QUESTIONS 251 and 252

5 OR 6

T. In *Superman II*, how many Kryptonian criminals escaped from the Phantom Zone?(3)
R. On *The Muppet Show*, who was the drummer for Dr. Teeth and the Electric Mayhem band?(1)
I. In *Archie* comics, what subject does Mr. Flutesnoot teach?(4)
V. What sport is played in a fronton with a cesta?(D)
I+. How many legs does a spider have?(5)
A. How many are in a quartet?(2)

QUESTIONS 251 and 252

1 OR 2

T. Conan
R. Miss Piggy
I. Archie
V. Wham-O
I+. Yellow and red
A. 144

251 and 252 ANSWERS

3 OR 4

T. Harrison Ford
R. Beaker
I. Mr. Weatherbee
V. Right in the middle of the head
I+. Six
A. Thirteen

251 and 252 ANSWERS

5 OR 6

T. Three
R. Animal
I. Science
V. Jai alai
I+. Eight
A. Four

251 and 252 ANSWERS

1 OR 2

T. In *The Empire Strikes Back*, who was the ruler of the Cloud City?(1)
R. What was the name of the starship in *Pigs in Space*?(3)
I. In *Archie* comics, what color is Miss Grundy's hair?(4)
V. In what sport are foils used?(5)
I+. If you were in the infantry, would you be in an underground storage room or in the army?(2)
A. What does the abbreviation Ltd. stand for in the names of companies?(6)

QUESTIONS 253 and 254

3 OR 4

T. In *The Empire Strikes Back*, who was frozen in carbonite?(1)
R. On *The Muppet Show*, what was the name of the doctor played by Rowlf the dog in *Veterinarian's Hospital*?(3)
I. In what comics will you find the character Dilton Doiley?(4)
V. What chess piece can only move diagonally?(5)
I+. If something has been petrified, has it turned into stone or has it been electrocuted?(2)
A. What does the abbreviation Inc. stand for in the names of companies?

QUESTIONS 253 and 254

5 OR 6

T. In *The Empire Strikes Back*, what was the name of Boba Fett's spaceship?(5)
R. What does Miss Piggy say just before she karate-chops someone?(2)
I. What is the name of Archie's best friend?(1)
V. In what sport do you try to knock over a mother-in-law and a widow with a ball?(D)
I+. If you were a sophomore, would you be a camel-herder or a student?(3)
A. What are the colors of the kind of cat known as magpie?(4)

QUESTIONS 253 and 254

1 OR 2

T. Lando Calrissian
R. *Swinetrek*
I. White
V. Fencing
I+. The army
A. Limited

253 and 254 ANSWERS

---

3 OR 4

T. Han Solo
R. Dr. Bob
I. *Archie*
V. The Bishop
I+. Turned into stone
A. Incorporated

253 and 254 ANSWERS

---

5 OR 6

T. *Slave 1*
R. "Hii-ya!" (or something to that effect)
I. Jughead
V. Bowling (a mother-in-law is the far-left pin; a widow is on the far right)
I+. A student
A. Black and white

253 and 254 ANSWERS

1 OR 2

T. What Walt Disney movie took place *inside* a computer?(2)
R. What team does Hannibal Smith lead?(1)
I. What is the name of Jughead's dog?(3)
V. How many holes are in a ten-pin bowling ball?(4)
I·. Is an inlet a body of water or a type of button hole?(5)
A. What is the one thing cats do all the time but no one has been able to figure out how they do it?(6)

QUESTIONS 255 and 256

3 OR 4

T. In *Return of the Jedi*, whose pet was Salacious Crumb?(3)
R. In *The A-Team*, who plays B.A. Baracus?(2)
I. In *Archie* comics, what is the name of Midge's boyfriend?(5)
V. In what game do you use a cue to slide a disc into a scoring triangle?(6)
I·. What happens to a deciduous tree in the fall?(4)
A. What does a speedometer measure?(1)

QUESTIONS 255 and 256

5 OR 6

T. In *Return of the Jedi*, what planet did Jabba the Hutt live on?(4)
R. In *Snork* cartoons, who has a pet octopus named Okky?(3)
I. In *Archie* comics, what does Jughead's hat look like?(5)
V. In what game do you use a mallet to drive a ball through a wicket?(1)
I·. How many known planets are there in our solar system?(2)
A. What fictional monster is based, in part, on the real-life Prince of Wallachia, Vlad the Impaler?(6)

QUESTIONS 255 and 256

1 OR 2

T. *Tron*
R. *The A-Team*
I. Hot Dog
V. Three
I+. A body of water
A. Purr

255 and 256 ANSWERS

---

3 OR 4

T. Jabba the Hutt's
R. Mr. T
I. Moose
V. Shuffleboard
I+. It loses its leaves
A. Speed

255 and 256 ANSWERS

---

5 OR 6

T. Tatooine
R. All Star
I. A crown
V. Croquet
I+. Nine
A. Dracula

255 and 256 ANSWERS

1 OR 2

T. What was the title of the second movie about Indiana Jones?(2)
R. What kind of vehicle was featured in the TV show *Blue Thunder*?(1)
I. In *Archie* comics, what is Reggie's last name?(5)
V. What is rubbed on the tip of a cue to keep it from slipping?(4)
I+. In what way are the children of sisters related to each other?(6)
A. By what name is Walt Disney's Experimental Prototype Community of Tomorrow theme park better known?(3)

QUESTIONS 261 and 262

---

3 OR 4

T. What superhero did actor Christopher Reeve play in the movies?(1)
R. Who eats Power Pellets?(2)
I. Of Archie's two girl friends, which one is rich?(3)
V. What do you use to support your pool cue when you must play an awkward angle and you can't use your hand?(6)
I+. In what way is a brother related to his brother's children?(5)
A. What kind of animal is Shamu?(4)

QUESTIONS 261 and 262

---

5 OR 6

T. In what movie did a computer say "The only way to win is not to play the game"?(1)
R. What cartoon characters are sometimes attacked by the Wartmongers?(2)
I. In *Archie* comics, what is Veronica's nickname?(3)
V. What is the name for the little diamonds imbedded in the sides of a pool table?(D)
I+. What relation is a sister to her brother's children?(4)
A. Valentina Tereshkova was the first woman ever to do what?(5)

QUESTIONS 261 and 262

1 OR 2

T. *Indiana Jones and the Temple of Doom*
R. A helicopter
I. Mantle
V. Chalk
I+. They are cousins
A. EPCOT Center

261 and 262 ANSWERS

3 OR 4

T. Superman
R. Pac-Man
I. Veronica
V. A bridge
I+. He's their uncle
A. A killer whale

261 and 262 ANSWERS

5 OR 6

T. *WarGames*
R. Smurfs
I. Ronnie
V. Sights
I+. Aunt
A. Travel in space (1963)

261 and 262 ANSWERS

1 OR 2

T. What kind of a spaceship did Luke Skywalker fly in *Star Wars*?(4)
R. What superhero's real name is Diana Prince?(1)
I. What are the colors of Iron Man's armor?(2)
V. How many points do you get for a bull's-eye in darts?(3)
I+. What color of light do you get when you mix red, yellow, and blue light?(6)
A. What kind of machine do the terms VHS and Beta refer to?(5)

QUESTIONS 263 and 264

3 OR 4

T. In *Star Wars*, what kind of creatures drove the Sand Crawler?(2)
R. What superhero is from Paradise Island?(3)
I. Where is the bottle city of Kandor kept?(4)
V. How many points do you get for a double bull's-eye in darts?(5)
I+. Where is your spinal cord?(1)
A. What do the letters P.H. stand for on an apartment-building elevator panel?(6)

QUESTIONS 263 and 264

5 OR 6

T. In *Star Wars*, what could you put on a droid to keep it from running away?(5)
R. What was the name of Mr. Bill's dog?(4)
I. From what planet is the bottle city of Kandor?(1)
V. What do you score if your dart lands on the board outside the double-score ring, away from the bull's-eye?(3)
I+. What does an isthmus connect, land or water?(2)
A What is a panda bear's favorite food?(6)

QUESTIONS 263 and 264

1 OR 2

T. An X-Wing Fighter
R. Wonder Woman
I. Gold (or yellow) and red
V. Twenty-five
I+. White light
A. Videotape recorders

263 and 264 ANSWERS

3 OR 4

T. Jawas
R. Wonder Woman
I. Superman's Fortress of Solitude
V. Fifty
I+. In your back
A. Penthouse

263 and 264 ANSWERS

5 OR 6

T. A restraining bolt
R. Spot
I. Krypton
V. Nothing
I+. Land
A. Bamboo shoots

263 and 264 ANSWERS

1 OR 2

T. In *Return of the Jedi*, who flew the *Millenium Falcon* with Nien Nubb?(3)
R. In *Muppet Babies*, which muppet has a computer?(1)
I. Who shrunk the bottle city of Kandor?(4)
V. What piece of sporting equipment is made up of a point, a barrel, a shaft, and a flight?(5)
I+. Is the element plutonium manufactured or mined?(2)
A. What is a koala bear's favorite food?(6)

QUESTIONS 265 and 266

3 OR 4

T. Who was Luke Skywalker's father?(1)
R. What is the name of the Snorks' submarine?(5)
I. What colors are Garfield the Cat?(2)
V. How many numbers appear on a regulation dartboard?(6)
I+. What is the square root of thirty-six: six or eighteen?(3)
A. On what continent would you find a koala bear?(4)

QUESTIONS 265 and 266

5 OR 6

T. In *The Last Starfighter*, what were the enemy aliens called?(3)
R. What show was Mr. Green Jeans on?(1)
I. What is the name of Garfield the Cat's owner?(4)
V. On a dartboard, which is closer to the middle: the double-score ring or the triple-score ring?(5)
I+. What hangs from a cave's ceiling: a stalagmite or a stalactite?(2)
A. What toy is called "The Construction Set of Tomorrow"?(6)

QUESTIONS 265 and 266

1 OR 2

T. Lando Calrissian
R. Scooter
I. Brainiac (in *Superman* comics)
V. A dart
I+. Manufactured
A. Eucalyptus leaves

265 and 266 ANSWERS

---

3 OR 4

T. Darth Vader
R. *Silver Fish*
I. Orange and black
V. Twenty
I+. Six
A. Australia

265 and 266 ANSWERS

---

5 OR 6

T. KO-DAN
R. *Captain Kangaroo*
I. Jon
V. The triple-score ring
I+. Stalactite (Think of *C* for ceiling, *G* for ground)
A. Capsela

265 and 266 ANSWERS

1 OR 2

T. In *The Last Starfighter*, what was the name of the alien who instructed Alex?(6)
R. What street does Big Bird live on?(1)
I. What is the name of Garfield the Cat's teddy bear?(2)
V. What kind of vehicle does Greg Hill ride?(5)
I+. Is ivory mined, made, or grown?(4)
A. What kind of kids have pets called koosas?(3)

QUESTIONS 311 and 312

---

3 OR 4

T. In *The Last Starfighter*, who tricked Alex into going to Rylos?(3)
R. What is Red Fraggle's favorite sport?(5)
I. In the *Garfield the Cat* comic strips, who is The World's Cutest Kitten?(4)
V. What floats on the water, has a mast and a sail but no sides, and isn't a sailboat?(6)
I+. Which place doesn't have any polar bears; the North Pole or the South Pole?(1)
A. In what ancient country were cats worshipped as gods?(2)

QUESTIONS 311 and 312

---

5 OR 6

T. In *The Last Starfighter*, what is the name of the game the aliens sent to Earth?(1)
R. What saying did Drew Barrymore make famous in *E.T.*?(5)
I. What is the name of Garfield the Cat's veterinarian?(6)
V. In what sport do you need a depth gauge?(3)
I+. Does a doctor use a stethoscope to look at the inside of your ears or listen to your chest?(2)
A. On computers, what do the initials IBM stand for?(4)

QUESTIONS 311 and 312

1 OR 2

T. Grig
R. Sesame Street
I. Pooky
V. A bicycle
I+. Grown (It comes from the tusks of elephant, walruses, and other animals)
A. Cabbage Patch Kids

311 and 312 ANSWERS

3 OR 4

T. Mr. Centauri
R. Swimming
I. Nermal
V. A windsurfer
I+. The South Pole
A. Egypt

311 and 312 ANSWERS

5 OR 6

T. *Starfighter*
R. "Give me a break!"
I. Liz
V. Underwater diving
I+. Listen to your chest
A. International Business Machines

311 and 312 ANSWERS

1 OR 2

T. What was the title of the third *Star Trek* movie?(3)
R. In *The A-Team*, what do B.A. Baracus's initials stand for?(4)
I. What is the name of Garfield the Cat's girl friend?(6)
V. What piece of sporting equipment has a canopy, a harness, and a rip cord?(5)
I+. How many are in a half-dozen?(1)
A. What was the name of the home video-game system made by Mattel?(2)

QUESTIONS 313 and 314

---

3 OR 4

T. In *Return of the Jedi*, which aliens lived on the moon of Endor?(5)
R. On what island did Mr. Roarke live?(1)
I. What superhero group does Doctor Doom usually fight?(2)
V. For what sport would you use pitons and ice screws?(6)
I+. How many legs in a herd of four cows?(4)
A. What is the name of the home computer made by Coleco?(3)

QUESTIONS 313 and 314

---

5 OR 6

T. In *Return of the Jedi*, what did the Ewoks think Threepio was?(4)
R. On what island did Tattoo work?(1)
I. Which superhero does Doctor Octopus usually fight?(2)
V. On what kind of animal would you put something with a horn, a pommel, and a cinch?(5)
I+. What gas is the first element in the listing of elements called the Periodic Table?(6)
A. Which company made the VCS home video game?(3)

QUESTIONS 313 and 314

1 OR 2

T. *The Search for Spock*
R. Bad Attitude
I. Arlene
V. A parachute
I+. Six
A. Intellivision (and Intellivision II)

313 and 314 ANSWERS

---

3 OR 4

T. Ewoks
R. Fantasy Island
I. Fantastic Four
V. Mountain climbing
I+. Sixteen
A. Adam

313 and 314 ANSWERS

---

5 OR 6

T. A god
R. Fantasy Island
I. Spider-man
V. A horse (Those are parts of a saddle)
I+. Hydrogen
A. Atari

313 and 314 ANSWERS

1 OR 2

T. In *Return of the Jedi*, in whose castle was the Pit of Rancor?(2)
R. Who owns Tweety Pie?(4)
I. What superhero does the Penguin usually fight?(1)
V. In what sport do the athletes wear "silks"?(5)
I+. How many Great Lakes are there?(6)
A. What do you call a person who designs houses and buildings?(3)

QUESTIONS 315 and 316

3 OR 4

T. In *Return of the Jedi*, what kind of alien was Admiral Ackbar? (And you can't say he was a fish!)(D)
R. Who says "I tot I taw a puddytat"?(2)
I. Which superhero does Lex Luthor usually fight?(1)
V. What is the maximum number of players that can be on a baseball field at one time, assuming the bases are loaded?(5)
I+. What does a Bunsen burner burn?(4)
A. Which side of a ship is called the starboard?(3)

QUESTIONS 315 and 316

5 OR 6

T. In *Return of the Jedi*, who was the first rebel to meet the Ewoks?(3)
R. Name one of the two TV shows that were hosted by Rod Serling.(4)
I. Which superhero does Mr. Freeze usually fight?(1)
V. In what kind of race is a sulky used?(5)
I+. How many frames of movie film are projected in one second?(6)
A. Which side of a ship is called the port?(2)

QUESTIONS 315 and 316

1 OR 2

T. Jabba's
R. Granny
I. The Batman
V. Horse racing
I+. Five
A. An architect

315 and 316 ANSWERS

---

3 OR 4

T. Mon Camari
R. Tweety Pie
I. Superman
V. Thirteen (nine from one team, four from the other)
I+. Gas
A. The right

315 and 316 ANSWERS

---

5 OR 6

T. Leia
R. *The Twilight Zone* or *Night Gallery*
I. Flash
V. Harness (sulky racing)
I+. Twenty-four
A. The left

315 and 316 ANSWERS

1 OR 2

T. In *Return of the Jedi*, what happened to Darth Vader? (2)
R. In cartoons, what does Dr. Bruce Banner turn into?(3)
I. What color are the Green Lantern's gloves?(4)
V. In what type of auto racing do only two cars race at a time?(5)
I+. What is the highest mountain in the world?(1)
A. What is the front of a ship called?(6)

QUESTIONS 321 and 322

3 OR 4

T. In *Return of the Jedi*, which spaceship flew into the Death Star and fired the shot that destroyed it?(2)
R. Where's the beef?(1)
I. On which hand does the Green Lantern wear his power ring?(3)
V. What type of car races in the Grand Prix?(D)
I+. Which planet has the highest-known mountain in our solar system?(5)
A. What is the back of a ship called?(4)

QUESTIONS 321 and 322

5 OR 6

T. In the movie *Alien*, what did the first stage of the monster's life cycle look like?(2)
R. What's the name of the friendly ghost?(1)
I. How long does Green Lantern's power ring keep its charge?(6)
V. What animal takes part in the sport of dressage?(4)
I+. What is the square root of twenty-five: five or 125?(5)
A. In Greek mythology, what was so special about the horse Pegasus?(3)

QUESTIONS 321 and 322

1 OR 2

T. He died
R. The Incredible Hulk
I. White
V. Drag racing
I+. Mount Everest
A. The bow

321 and 322 ANSWERS

---

3 OR 4

T. The *Millennium Falcon*
R. At Wendy's
I. His right hand
V. Formula One
I+. Mars (The mountain is called Mons Olympus)
A. The stern

321 and 322 ANSWERS

---

5 OR 6

T. An egg
R. Casper
I. Twenty-four hours
V. A horse
I+. Five
A. It had wings

321 and 322 ANSWERS

1 OR 2

T. In *Return of the Jedi*, what color was the energy that came from the Emperor's fingers?(2)
R. What is the name of Daisy's pet in *Pole Position*?(4)
I. Who says "In brightest day, in blackest night, no evil shall escape my sight"?(3)
V. How is a King different from ordinary pieces in a game of checkers?(5)
I+. In the wild, what do pink flamingoes eat that makes them pink?(6)
A. In legends, how is the unicorn different from other horses?(1)

QUESTIONS 323 and 324

3 OR 4

T. What kind of an alien was Chewbacca?(5)
R. Who had adventures with a horse called Pokey?(1)
I. What superhero's real name is Hal Jordan?(6)
V. Name the suits in a deck of cards.(2)
I+. What special ability does the animal called a chameleon have?(3)
A. What restaurant advertises with this phrase: "You, you're the one"?(4)

QUESTIONS 323 and 324

5 OR 6

T. Who lived in Never-Never Land?(3)
R. What was the name of the bully who was always trying to smash Mr. Bill?(4)
I. What symbol is on the front of Flash's costume?(5)
V. How many cards are in a standard deck?(1)
I+. What does a snake use to sniff the air?(6)
A. What is the monster known as Gojira in Japan called in English?(2)

QUESTIONS 323 and 324

1 OR 2

T. Blue
R. Kooma
I. Green Lantern
V. The King is made by stacking two checkers one on top of the other
I+. Shrimps
A. The unicorn has a horn in the middle of its forehead

323 and 324 ANSWERS

3 OR 4

T. A wookie
R. Gumby
I. Green Lantern
V. Diamonds, hearts, clubs, and spades
I+. It can change its skin color to blend in with its background
A. McDonald's

323 and 324 ANSWERS

5 OR 6

T. Peter Pan
R. Sluggo
I. A lightning bolt
V. Fifty-two
I+. Its tongue
A. Godzilla

323 and 324 ANSWERS

1 OR 2

T. What did Peter Pan want Wendy to sew back on him?(3)
R. On what live-action show did the Fonz first appear?(4)
I. What color is Flash's costume?(5)
V. In a standard deck of cards, how many cards are in each suit?(6)
I+. What is the most important single bee in a hive?(1)
A. What animal does ham come from?(2)

QUESTIONS 325 and 326

3 OR 4

T. What scary movie showed the glowing red eyes of Jody the Pig?(6)
R. What color is Cookie Monster?(3)
I. Where does Flash keep his costume when he assumes his secret identity?(4)
V. What is the highest number to appear on a single card in a standard deck of cards?(5)
I+. What is the closest star to Earth?(1)
A. What does a thermometer measure?(2)

QUESTIONS 325 and 326

5 OR 6

T. In *Monty Python and the Holy Grail*, what did the knights use to make the sound of hoofbeats?(2)
R. Who was always fighting the Daleks?(1)
I. What city does Flash live in?(3)
V. In backgammon, how many pieces does each player begin with?(5)
I+. Between which two planets is the Asteroid belt?(4)
A. What does an odometer measure?(6)

QUESTIONS 325 and 326

1 OR 2

T. His shadow
R. *Happy Days*
I. Red
V. Thirteen
I+. The queen
A. A pig

325 and 326 ANSWERS

3 OR 4

T. *The Amityville Horror*
R. Blue
I. In his ring
V. Ten
I+. The sun
A. Temperature

325 and 326 ANSWERS

5 OR 6

T. Coconut shells
R. Dr. Who
I. Central City
V. Fifteen
I+. Mars and Jupiter
A. Distance traveled

325 and 326 ANSWERS

1 OR 2

T. In *Return of the Jedi*, what was Wicket the Ewok's full name?(5)
R. On *Fraggle Rock*, what do Doozers make their Doozer Stix from?(4)
I. Which superhero is known as The World's Greatest Detective?(1)
V. What is the name of the special die used for gambling in backgammon?(6)
I+. What is the Prince of Wales's first name?(2)
A. Which cereal is supposed to make the sounds *snap*, *crackle*, *pop*?(3)

QUESTIONS 331 and 332

3 OR 4

T. What were the computer motorcycles in *Tron* called?(5)
R. On the *Star Wars Holiday Special*, what was the name of Chewbacca's son?(D)
I. Which superhero is known as The Scarlet Speedster?(1)
V. How many sets of numbers does an individual domino tile have?(3)
I+. What is the Princess of Wales's first name?(2)
A. Which cereal is shaped like the letters of the alphabet?(4)

QUESTIONS 331 and 332

5 OR 6

T. What was the original title of *Return of the Jedi*?(6)
R. On TV, what was M*A*S*H's unit number?(4)
I. What color is the bat on the front of Batgirl's costume?(2)
V. In a game of chess, how many pawns does each player start out with?(5)
I+. What is the name of the Queen of England?(1)
A. What came out of Aladdin's lamp?(3)

QUESTIONS 331 and 332

1 OR 2

T. Wicket W. Warrick
R. Radishes
I. The Batman
V. The doubling cube
I+. Charles
A. Rice Krispies

331 and 332 ANSWERS

---

3 OR 4

T. Lightcycles
R. Lumpy
I. Flash
V. Two
I+. Diana
A. Alphabits

331 and 332 ANSWERS

---

5 OR 6

T. *Revenge of the Jedi*
R. 4077
I. Yellow
V. Eight
I+. Elizabeth (II)
A. A genie

331 and 332 ANSWERS

1 OR 2

T. What color is Superman's cape?(2)
R. What kind of vehicle was featured in the TV show *Air Wolf*?(1)
I. In *The Batman* comics, what is the other identity of the Police Commissioner's daughter?(4)
V. What kind of car race starts with lights flashing on something called a Christmas tree?(5)
I+. What causes tides?(3)
A. What is Donald Duck's middle name?(D)

QUESTIONS 333

3 OR 4

T. Where is Superman's Fortress of Solitude?(1)
R. What were Curly, Larry, and Moe called?(2)
I. What job does Batgirl do when she assumes her secret identity?(4)
V. In what kind of flying vehicle do passengers ride in a basket?(5)
I+. How many letters are in the alphabet?(3)
A. In what month do Canadians celebrate Thanksgiving?(6)

QUESTIONS 333

5 OR 6

T. When Zolo was trying to kill Joan Wilder in *Romancing the Stone*, who pushed him into the alligator pit?(6)
R. Who is Aunt Fritzi's niece?(5)
I. In what city does Batgirl live?(4)
V. What do you do with an ultralight?(3)
I+. What is organized according to the Dewey Decimal System?(2)
A. In what month do we celebrate St. Valentine's Day?(1)

QUESTIONS 333

1 OR 2

T. Red
R. A helicopter
I. Batgirl
V. Drag races
I·. The gravitational pull of the moon
A. Fauntleroy

333 ANSWERS

3 OR 4

T. The North Pole
R. The Three Stooges
I. She is an American congresswoman
V. A balloon
I·. Twenty-six
A. October

333 ANSWERS

5 OR 6

T. Joan Wilder
R. Nancy
I. Washington, D.C.
V. Fly
I·. Library books
A. February

333 ANSWERS

1 OR 2

T. In *Superman II*, what kind of vehicle was thrown at Superman?(6)
R. In *The Littles*, which Little wears a purple bow on her tail?(5)
I. Which superhero is known as The Man of Steel?(1)
V. Which home computer comes with a Smartwriter?(4)
I+. How many legs are in a flock of six chickens?(3)
A. What machines were called horseless carriages when they were first made?(2)

QUESTIONS 334

3 OR 4

T. What kind of magic musical instrument did the Smurfs have to find in their movie?(6)
R. What was Corporal O'Reilly's nickname in *M*A*S*H*?(3)
I. Which superhero is known as The Emerald Gladiator?(2)
V. How many color segments are on a Simon game?(5)
I+. How many eyes are in a school of eight fish?(4)
A. What kind of a theater does Shelly Duvall run?(1)

QUESTIONS 334

5 OR 6

T. In *Superman III*, where did Clark Kent and Superman have their fight?(2)
R. What was Captain Pierce's nickname in *M*A*S*H*?(1)
I. In the cartoon strip *Bloom County*, what kind of an animal is Opus?(6)
V. How many squares are on the game board of Mattel's electronic version of *Dungeons and Dragons*?(5)
I+. How many manes are in a pride of nine lions?(3)
A. Which car company makes the Mustang?(4)

QUESTIONS 334

1 OR 2

T. A bus
R. Lucy
I. Superman
V. Adam
I·. Twelve
A. Cars

334 ANSWERS

---

3 OR 4

T. A flute
R. Radar
I. Green Lantern
V. Four
I·. Sixteen
A. *Fairie Tale Theater*

334 ANSWERS

---

5 OR 6

T. A car junkyard
R. Hawkeye
I. A penguin
V. Sixty-four
I·. Nine
A. Ford

334 ANSWERS

1 OR 2

T. In *The Wizard of Oz*, what did the Tin Man want from the Wizard?(4)
R. On *M*A*S*H*, who was the man who wore dresses?(3)
I. Which superhero does the red-skinned Sinestro usually fight?(6)
V. Which video game won the Arkie award for Best Arcade Game of 1980?(5)
I+. Name a mammal that is covered with sharp quills.(2)
A. Which soft drink does Bill Cosby advertise?(1)

QUESTIONS 335 and 336

3 OR 4

T. In *The Wizard of Oz*, what blew Dorothy to Oz?(5)
R. On *M*A*S*H*, what was Margaret Houlihan's nickname?(1)
I. What symbol is on the front of Captain America's costume?(3)
V. Which video game won the Arkie award for Best Arcade Game of 1981 *and* 1982?(4)
I+. If you were in a stockade, would you be in an old railway tunnel or in a wooden fort?(2)
A. What is the main ingredient in Coca-Cola?(6)

QUESTIONS 335 and 336

5 OR 6

T. What kind of animals were *The Rescuers*?(3)
R. During which war did *M*A*S*H* take place?(4)
I. What does Captain America carry?(5)
V. What is the only game control used in a *Pac-Man* game?(1)
I+. Is a predecessor someone who comes before you, or someone who comes after you?(2)
A. Which car company makes the Civic?(6)

QUESTIONS 335 and 336

1 OR 2

T. A heart
R. Corporal (Max) Klinger
I. Green Lantern
V. *Space Invaders*
I+. Porcupine, hedgehog, or spiny anteater
A. Coca-Cola

335 and 336 ANSWERS

3 OR 4

T. A tornado
R. Hot Lips
I. A white star
V. *Asteroids*
I+. A wooden fort
A. Water

335 and 336 ANSWERS

5 OR 6

T. Mice
R. Korean War
I. A shield
V. A joystick
I+. Someone who comes before you
A. Honda

335 and 336 ANSWERS

1 OR 2

T. Whose life did Superman save by flying back in time at the end of *Superman*?(1)
R. What superhero group does the Ice Man belong to?(3)
I. What are the colors of Spider-man's costume?(4)
V. What happens to the monsters when Pac-Man eats an Energizer?(2)
I+. Which two bodies of water are joined by the Strait of Gibraltar?(5)
A. What is the fastest moving animal?(D)

QUESTIONS 341 and 342

3 OR 4

T. What was Indiana wearing when he first appeared in the second Indiana Jones movie?(4)
R. In what TV show did Eddie Murphy and Joe Piscopo first star together?(3)
I. In what city does Spider-man live?(1)
V. How many points can you score if Pac-Man eats all four monsters during one Energizer attack?(5)
I+. Is there such a thing as the dark side of the moon?(2)
A. Which animal has the largest eye?(6)

QUESTIONS 341 and 342

5 OR 6

T. In *Superman*, what did Superman have to chase after he got out of the swimming pool?(5)
R. How many Angels were there on *Charlie's Angels*?(1)
I. Are Spider-man's webshooters on the front of his hands or the back of his hands?(2)
V. How many bonus Pac-Mans can you get in a single game?(3)
I+. On Earth, we can see the moon rise and set. If we were on the moon, could we see Earth rise and set?(4)
A. What movie company designed the video game called *Ballblazer*?(6)

QUESTIONS 341 and 342

1 OR 2

T. Lois Lane's
R. The X-Men
I. Black and white
V. They turn blue (and run away)
I+. The Atlantic Ocean and the Mediterranean Sea
A. The peregrine falcon (217 mph.)

3 OR 4

T. A white tuxedo (suit)
R. *Saturday Night Live*
I. New York
V. 3,000
I+. No (In the course of a month, the sun shines over all of the moon)
A. The giant squid

341 and 342 ANSWERS

5 OR 6

T. Missiles (with nuclear warheads)
R. Three
I. The back of his hands
V. Only one
I+. No (Since the moon always keeps the same face to the Earth, Earth would always seem to be in the same spot in the sky)
A. Lucasfilm (makers of *Star Wars*)

341 and 342 ANSWERS

1 OR 2

T. In *Superman II*, what Paris landmark was nearly blown up?(3)
R. What is the name of the doctor who comes from the planet Galifrey?(4)
I. What superhero group has its headquarters in New York's Baxter Building?(6)
V. How many squares are on a chessboard?(5)
I+. Which is the largest ocean on Earth?(1)
A. Which company made the computer called the VIC-20?(2)

QUESTIONS 343 and 344

3 OR 4

T. Where did Lois Lane and Clark Kent go at the beginning of *Superman II*?(4)
R. What is the name of the Sesame Street character who loves to eat cookies?(1)
I. What happened to Captain America at the end of World War II?(6)
V. In chess, what is the maximum number of squares a pawn may advance on its first move?(2)
I+. Which country has the most land?(5)
A. Which toy company makes the plastic Cabbage Patch Kids?(3)

QUESTIONS 343 and 344

5 OR 6

T. What was Superman's name on his home planet?(2)
R. What is the name of the kid who starred in *Silver Spoons*?(5)
I. Which superhero does the Red Skull usually fight?(6)
V. What is the name of the chess piece that usually looks like a horse?(1)
I+. The largest island in the world is also a country. Name it.(3)
A. Which one of these monsters has Godzilla never battled: Mothra, King Kong, Gorgo, or Megalon?(4)

QUESTIONS 343 and 344

1 OR 2

T. The Eiffel Tower
R. Dr. Who
I. Fantastic Four
V. Sixty-four
I+. The Pacific
A. Commodore

343 and 344 ANSWERS

3 OR 4

T. Niagara Falls
R. Cookie Monster
I. He was frozen in a block of ice
V. Two
I+. USSR (or the Soviet Union, or Russia)
A. Coleco

343 and 344 ANSWERS

5 OR 6

T. Kal-el
R. Ricky Schroeder
I. Captain America
V. A Knight
I+. Greenland (Australia is a continent)
A. Gorgo

343 and 344 ANSWERS

1 OR 2

T. What was the title of the movie in which Sark sent useless programs to die on the Game Grid?(2)
R. Who sings "It's a Beautiful Day in the Neighborhood"?(1)
I. Which World War II soldier went on to become the head agent of S.H.I.E.L.D.?(5)
V. Which chess piece moves in an L-shaped pattern?(4)
I+. What is the largest lake in the world?(D)
A. What do coffee beans grow on: trees, bushes, or roots?(3)

QUESTIONS 345 and 346

3 OR 4

T. In *Time Bandits*, what came out of the wardrobe cupboard in Kevin's bedroom?(5)
R. What is the title of the cartoon show based on the game *Dungeons and Dragons*?(1)
I. What do the initials S.H.I.E.L.D. stand for?(6)
V. In *Monopoly*, how many properties does each player begin the game with?(2)
I+. Which is the largest of the Great Lakes?(4)
A. For the television network, what do the initials ABC stand for?(3)

QUESTIONS 345 and 346

5 OR 6

T. What was the name of the brand-new starship that Scotty broke on purpose in the third *Star Trek* movie?(4)
R. What can Aquaman breathe that other people can't?(1)
I. Where is S.H.I.E.L.D.'s headquarters?(5)
V. What board game has kings and double-jumps?(2)
I+. Is a light-year a unit of time or a unit of distance?(3)
A. Where are your metatarsals?(6)

QUESTIONS 345 and 346

1 OR 2

T. *Tron*
R. Mr. Rogers
I. Nick Fury
V. The Knight
I+. The Caspian Sea
A. Bushes

345 and 346 ANSWERS

---

3 OR 4

T. A knight (in armor and on horseback)
R. *Dungeons and Dragons*
I. Supreme Headquarters International Espionage, Law Enforcement Division
V. None
I+. Lake Superior
A. American Broadcasting Company

345 and 346 ANSWERS

---

5 OR 6

T. U.S.S. *Excelsior*
R. Water
I. On board the Helicarrier
V. Checkers
I+. A unit of distance
A. In your feet (They are bones)

345 and 346 ANSWERS

1 OR 2

T. What was the name of the elephant that flew with Timothy the mouse?(1)
R. What kind of animal is shown at the end of every TV show made by Mary Tyler Moore Productions?(2)
I. Which comic book character is The Pin-up Queen?(5)
V. In poker, what is a Royal Flush?(6)
I+. Would you find a meteorite on Earth or in space?(3)
A. What is the more common name for the planet Terra?(4)

QUESTIONS 351 and 352

3 OR 4

T. What did Dumbo hold in his trunk so he could fly?(2)
R. Whose apartment did Mork live in?(1)
I. What do readers contribute to each Katy Keene comic?(6)
V. In Cribbage, how many points do you get for turning up a Jack on the cut?(5)
I+. Which is the largest state in the U.S.A.?(3)
A. What is the more common name for the object in space called Luna?(4)

QUESTIONS 351 and 352

5 OR 6

T. In *Snow White and the Seven Dwarfs*, who was the only dwarf who didn't speak?(3)
R. In *Chip 'n' Dale* cartoons, which one has the red nose?(2)
I. What is the nickname of Katy Keene's boyfriend?(4)
V. In Cribbage, what number must your cards total before you get two points?(5)
I+. In what year did people first land on the moon?(6)
A. What make of computer is advertised on TV by a Charlie Chaplin look-alike?(1)

QUESTIONS 351 and 352

1 OR 2

T. Dumbo
R. A kitten
I. Katy Keene
V. Ten, Jack, Queen, King, and Ace, all in the same suit
I+. On Earth (Meteoroids are found in space, and a meteor is what we see streaking through the sky)
A. Earth

351 and 352 ANSWERS

3 OR 4

T. A feather
R. Mindy's
I. The designs for all her clothes
V. One
I+. Texas
A. The moon

351 and 352 ANSWERS

5 OR 6

T. Dopey (But he did scream once)
R. Dale
I. K.O.
V. Fifteen
I+. 1969
A. IBM (PC, PCjr)

351 and 352 ANSWERS

1 OR 2

T. In *Snow White and the Seven Dwarfs*, what did Snow White bite into that made her sleep?(1)
R. What's the name of the little girl in comic books who loves polka dots?(2)
I. In *Archie* comics, what is Veronica's last name?(6)
V. What color are the triple-word-score squares on a *Scrabble* board?(5)
I⁺. Which planet is closest to Earth?(3)
A. What is the language spoken by the greatest number of people in the world?(4)

QUESTIONS 353 and 354

---

3 OR 4

T. In *Snow White and the Seven Dwarfs*, what was the name of the dwarf who couldn't stay awake?(1)
R. What color is Garfield the Cat's nose?(4)
I. In *Archie* comics, what is the name of Veronica's butler?(6)
V. What color are the double-word-score squares on a *Scrabble* board?(5)
I⁺. In what part of your body does the digestion of food begin?(2)
A. Is English the first, second, or fifth most common language in the world?(3)

QUESTIONS 353 and 354

---

5 OR 6

T. In *Snow White and the Seven Dwarfs*, what was the name of the dwarf who kept sneezing?(1)
R. In cartoons, what is the name of the Incredible Hulk's teenage friend?(4)
I. In *Archie* comics, what is the name of the soda shop where the kids usually hang out?(5)
V. In *Monopoly*, what must you do if you roll doubles three times in a row?(2)
I⁺. On a calendar, what is usually the first day of each week?(3)
A. Which language has the most words?(6)

QUESTIONS 353 and 354

1 OR 2

T. A poisoned apple
R. Little Dot
I. Lodge
V. Red
I+. Venus
A. Chinese (Mandarin)

353 and 354 ANSWERS

---

3 OR 4

T. Sleepy
R. Pink
I. Smithers
V. Pink
I+. Your mouth
A. Second

353 and 354 ANSWERS

---

5 OR 6

T. Sneezy
R. Rick Jones
I. Pop's Choklit Shoppe
V. Go to jail
I+. Sunday
A. English (approximately 790,000)

353 and 354 ANSWERS

1 OR 2

T. What did Mary Poppins hold on to when she flew?(2)
R. On the *Dungeons and Dragons* cartoon show, who led the kids on their adventures?(3)
I. In *Archie* comics, what is the name of Archie's music group?(4)
V. What video game is the "sequel" to the game *Defender*?(6)
I+. What common device is Marconi noted for inventing?(5)
A. What is the most common last name in the English language?(1)

QUESTIONS 355 and 356

3 OR 4

T. What was the name of the Nanny who could slide *up* the bannister?(1)
R. At the beginning of the *Dungeons and Dragons* cartoon show, how did the kids get to the world of Dungeons and Dragons?(3)
I. In *Archie* comics, what is the name of Veronica's mischief-making little cousin?(5)
V. How do you get bonus points in the video game *Frogger*?(4)
I+. Is your surname your first name or your last name?(2)
A. Who is noted for kids' entertainment and has won more Oscars than anyone else?(6)

QUESTIONS 355 and 356

5 OR 6

T. Into what kind of drawings did Mary Poppins take Burt and the kids?(6)
R. Where do Power Pellets grow?(4)
I. In *Archie* comics, what does Miss Beazly do?(5)
V. What game is played with a ball and a net in a swimming pool?(1)
I+. Is a promontory someone who works backstage in a theater or a body of land sticking out into water?(2)
A. Does lightning ever strike the same place twice?(3)

QUESTIONS 355 and 356

1 OR 2

T. An umbrella
R. The Dungeon Master
I. The Archies
V. *Star Gate*
I+. The radio
A. Smith

355 and 356 ANSWERS

3 OR 4

T. Mary Poppins
R. They role a Dungeons and Dragons roller coaster at an amusement park
I. Leroy
V. By eating waterbugs or flies
I+. Your last name
A. Walt Disney

355 and 356 ANSWERS

5 OR 6

T. Chalk drawings (on a sidewalk)
R. Pac Forest
I. She runs the high-school cafeteria
V. Water polo
I+. A body of land sticking out into water
A. Yes (The CN Tower has been hit up to 200 times in one year)

355 and 356 ANSWERS

1 OR 2

T. What kind of animals starred in *The Secret of NIMH*?(5)
R. What's the name of the cartoon skunk who always falls in love with cats who have a white streak down their backs?(4)
I. In *Archie* comics, whose parents are Fred and Mary?(3)
V. What game did David *start* to play with the defense computer in *WarGames*, though the computer didn't think it was a game?(6)
I+. What letter is the Roman numeral for five?(2)
A. Which reindeer had a red nose?(1)

QUESTIONS 361 and 362

3 OR 4

T. What kind of animals starred in *Watership Down*?(3)
R. In *The Mary Tyler Moore Show*, what kind of place did Mary work at?(2)
I. What is the name of the high-school coach in *Archie* comics?(6)
V. How do you start a game of Fifty-two Pick-up?(4)
I+. What letter is the Roman numeral for ten?(5)
A. How many finger holes are there in a telephone dial?(1)

QUESTIONS 361 and 362

5 OR 6

T. Where did Dumbo have to work?(2)
R. Where does Pac-Man live?(3)
I. In *Archie* comics, what is Pop's last name?(6)
V. How many screens must you clear before you are faced with two Qix, in the game of the same name?(5)
I+. What letter is the Roman numeral for one?(1)
A. On what island do Godzilla and the rest of his monstrous friends live?(4)

QUESTIONS 361 and 362

1 OR 2

T. Rats
R. Pepe Le Pew
I. Archie's
V. *Global Thermonuclear War*
I+. V
A. Rudolph

361 and 362 ANSWERS

---

3 OR 4

T. Rabbits
R. A TV station
I. Coach Kleats
V. You throw a deck of cards onto the floor
I+. X
A. Ten

361 and 362 ANSWERS

---

5 OR 6

T. A circus
R. Pac Land
I. Tate
V. Two
I+. I
A. Monster Island

361 and 362 ANSWERS

1 OR 2

T. In *Bambi*, what kind of an animal was Flower?(2)
R. What was the title of the first TV movie in which aliens in orange suits *looked* like humans but were really green lizards?(3)
I. In *Archie* comics, what is the name of the high school's janitor?(5)
V. On what item of clothing are friendship pins usually worn?(6)
I+. What letter is the Roman numeral for one hundred?(4)
A. What is the name for the last railroad car in a train?(1)

QUESTIONS 363 and 364

3 OR 4

T. In *Bambi*, what kind of animal was Thumper?(2)
R. In *Star Trek*, what was Captain James Kirk's middle initial?(3)
I. In *Archie* comics, what does Archie call his car?(5)
V. What is the only "equipment" you need to play Scissors, Paper, Stone?(4)
I+. What letter is the Roman numeral for 1,000?(6)
A. What is the name for the special type of ship that can travel underwater?(1)

QUESTIONS 363 and 364

5 OR 6

T. What kind of animal was Bambi?(3)
R. In *Star Trek*, what was the doctor's nickname?(1)
I. In *Archie* comics, what color is Archie's car?(4)
V. What should your strategy be in *Space Invaders*: to shoot the aliens row by row or column by column?(2)
I+. What letter is the Roman numeral for fifty?(6)
A. What is John Dykstra noted for?(5)

QUESTIONS 363 and 364

1 OR 2

T. A skunk
R. *V*
I. Mr. Svenson
V. Shoes
I+. C
A. Caboose

363 and 364 ANSWERS

---

3 OR 4

T. A rabbit
R. T.
I. Ol' Betsy
V. Your hands
I+. M
A. Submarine

363 and 364 ANSWERS

---

5 OR 6

T. A baby deer (or fawn)
R. Bones
I. Red
V. Column by column
I+. L
A. Movie special effects (especially *Star Wars*)

363 and 364 ANSWERS

1 OR 2

T. What did the little boy call the horse in *The Black Stallion*?(3)
R. What is the name of the ghost horse in *Casper* cartoons?(4)
I. What does Daredevil have strapped to his left leg?(5)
V. What video game insults you by shouting out "Chicken! Come back and fight like a robot!" when your player runs away?(6)
I+. Which has more mass, a kilogram of lead or a kilogram of feathers?(2)
A. What do firefighters attach their hoses to in order to get water?(1)

QUESTIONS 365 and 366

3 OR 4

T. In *The Black Stallion*, what caused the boy and the horse to end up on the island?(5)
R. What is the group of three bad ghosts in *Casper* cartoons called?(6)
I. What is printed on the front of Daredevil's costume?(4)
V. What do you try to shoot in the video game *Berzerk*?(3)
I+. What is the capital city of England?(2)
A. On what island is Mount Crunchmore?(1)

QUESTIONS 365 and 366

5 OR 6

T. What did the horse win at the end of *The Black Stallion*?(2)
R. What color is Tweety Pie?(3)
I. What superhero does the Kingpin usually fight?(5)
V. What is the name of the bouncing happy face in the video game *Berzerk*?(6)
I+. What is a baby cow called?(1)
A. Which toy company makes *Star Wars* action figures?(4)

QUESTIONS 365 and 366

1 OR 2

T. The Black
R. Nightmare
I. His billy club (or cane)
V. *Berzerk*
I+. Their masses are the same—one kilogram (Trick question!)
A. A hydrant

365 and 366 ANSWERS

3 OR 4

T. Their ship sank
R. The Ghostly Trio
I. The initials DD
V. Robots
I+. London
A. Crunch Island

365 and 366 ANSWERS

5 OR 6

T. A race
R. Yellow
I. Daredevil
V. Evil Otto
I+. Calf
A. Kenner

365 and 366 ANSWERS

1 OR 2

T. What is the title of the second movie in *The Black Stallion* series?(2)
R. Which Snork is green and can't talk?(1)
I. In the *Garfield the Cat* comic strips, where do his owner's parents live?(3)
V. Name two of the four things that can kill your player in the video game *Berzerk*.(4)
I+. How many grams are in a kilogram?(5)
A. Which toy company makes Care Bear plastic dolls?(6)

QUESTIONS 411 and 412

---

3 OR 4

T. What movie features the song "Just a Spoonful of Sugar Helps the Medicine Go Down"?(4)
R. Who is Robin the Frog's uncle?(1)
I. Why is Supergirl's hair color different from the hair color of her secret identity?(2)
V. In which video game must you avoid flippers, spinners, and spikes?(3)
I+. At how many degrees Celsius does water boil at sea level?(5)
A. What picture does Funshine Bear have on its tummy?(6)

QUESTIONS 411 and 412

---

5 OR 6

T. What movie introduced the word "Supercalifragilisticexpialadocious"?(1)
R. Which muppet is known as The Great?(4)
I. In comic books, who is Dr. Katherine Waynesboro's associate in the study of gamma rays?(5)
V. How many different types of UFOs are there in the video game *Asteroids*?(2)
I+. What device is Alexander Graham Bell noted for inventing?(3)
A. What other *Star Wars* character comes with the Jabba the Hutt action figure?(6)

QUESTIONS 411 and 412

1 OR 2

T. *The Black Stallion Returns*
R. Tooter
I. On a farm
V. Robots, bullets, walls, or the bouncing happy face
I+. 1,000
A. Kenner

411 and 412 ANSWERS

3 OR 4

T. *Mary Poppins*
R. Kermit
I. She wears a wig as part of her disguise
V. *Tempest*
I+. 100°C
A. A sun

411 and 412 ANSWERS

5 OR 6

T. *Mary Poppins*
R. Gonzo
I. Dr. Bruce Banner
V. Two
I+. The telephone
A. Salacious Crumb

411 and 412 ANSWERS

1 OR 2

T. In *Poltergeist*, what was the house built on top of?(4)
R. On *The Muppet Show*, who is in love with Carmella the Chicken?(5)
I. What color is the Incredible Hulk's hair?(1)
V. What company makes the arcade version of the game *Tempest*?(6)
I+. What kind of book contains a list of words and their meanings?(2)
A. How many bits are in 1 K of computer memory storage: 996, 1,000, or 1,024?(3)

QUESTIONS 413 and 414

3 OR 4

T. In *Poltergeist*, what did the little girl say when the spirits went inside the TV set?(1)
R. What is Alvin the Chipmunk's favorite instrument?(2)
I. In the comic books, what was the source of the gamma rays that Bruce Banner was exposed to?(5)
V. What company makes the arcade version of the game *Asteroids*?(4)
I+. What do you call a book that contains nothing but maps?(3)
A. What was the name of the home computer made by Mattel?(D)

QUESTIONS 413 and 414

5 OR 6

T. In *Poltergeist*, what reached in through the window to grab at the little boy?(2)
R. What is the name of the sword carried by Thundarr the Barbarian?(6)
I. Which comic book hero is Master of the Mystic Arts?(5)
V. In what video game must you avoid mutants, swarmers, and baiters?(3)
I+. What is in the middle of most living cells?(4)
A. What cereal is advertised by the Wizard of Words?(1)

QUESTIONS 413 and 414

1 OR 2

T. A graveyard
R. Gonzo
I. Green
V. Atari
I+. A dictionary
A. 1,024

413 and 414 ANSWERS

---

3 OR 4

T. "They're here."
R. The harmonica
I. A gamma-bomb explosion
V. Atari
I+. An atlas
A. Aquarius (Intellivision is a video game)

413 and 414 ANSWERS

---

5 OR 6

T. A tree
R. Sunsword
I. Dr. Strange
V. *Defender*
I+. Nucleus
A. Alphabits

413 and 414 ANSWERS

1 OR 2

T. In *Poltergeist*, what kind of a doll tried to kill the little boy?(4)
R. What kind of animal is Foghorn Leghorn?(5)
I. What is Dr. Strange's first name?(6)
V. In what video game must you avoid springese, foxfires, and barrels?(3)
I+. How many sides does a triangle have?(2)
A. What two soft drinks would you taste if you took part in the Pepsi Challenge?(1)

QUESTIONS 415 and 416

---

3 OR 4

T. In *E.T.*, what did Elliot step on when he ran back inside the house?(3)
R. Who played Mindy on *Mork and Mindy*?(4)
I. Whose amulet contains the all-seeing eye of Agamotto?(6)
V. In what video game must you avoid droid ships, command ships, and death ships?(5)
I+. How many sides does a square have?(1)
A. Where would you find the Don Martin Department?(2)

QUESTIONS 415 and 416

---

5 OR 6

T. What did Michael Jackson turn into at the beginning of *Thriller*?(3)
R. What superhero is helped by Steve Trevor?(5)
I. Which superhero does Brainiac usually fight?(4)
V. In what video game do waves of birds protect their mothership?(1)
I+. How many sides does a cube have?(6)
A. Who created Mickey Mouse?(2)

QUESTIONS 415 and 416

1 OR 2

T. A clown doll
R. A rooster
I. Steven
V. *Donkey Kong*
I+. Three
A. Pepsi-Cola and Coca-Cola

415 and 416 ANSWERS

---

3 OR 4

T. A pizza
R. Pam Dawber
I. Dr. Strange
V. *Omega Race*
I+. Four
A. *MAD* magazine

415 and 416 ANSWERS

---

5 OR 6

T. A werewolf
R. Wonder Woman
I. Superman
V. *Phoenix*
I+. Six
A. Walt Disney

415 and 416 ANSWERS

1 OR 2

T. What scary actor did the "rap" on Michael Jackson's *Thriller*?(5)
R. On *Fantasy Island*, what did Tattoo say at the beginning of every show?(4)
I. What is the name of the Inhumans' teleporting dog?(6)
V. What game cartridge was originally given away with Colecovision video games?(3)
I·. Is the porpoise a fish or a mammal?(1)
A. What company first made the Walkman?(2)

QUESTIONS 421 and 422

3 OR 4

T. What color were most of Michael Jackson's clothes in *Thriller*?(1)
R. What does Green Lantern use to recharge his power ring?(4)
I. Where is the Inhumans' city of Attilan located?(5)
V. What is the name of the character who stars in the video game called *Pitfall*?(3)
I·. Which is the smallest state in the U.S.A.?(2)
A. What does a Compact Disc record player use insead of a needle?(6)

QUESTIONS 421 and 422

5 OR 6

T. What happened to the car at the beginning of Michael Jackson's *Thriller*?(1)
R. On what TV show did a helicopter pilot play the cello?(3)
I. Which Inhuman can use her hair like tentacles?(4)
V. How many keypad squares are there on a Colecovision game controller?(5)
I·. Is a tomato a fruit, a vegetable, or a berry?(6)
A. Who created Donald Duck?(2)

QUESTIONS 421 and 422

1 OR 2

T. Vincent Price
R. "The plane, the plane!"
I. Lockjaw
V. *Donkey Kong*
I+. A mammal
A. Sony

421 and 422 ANSWERS

3 OR 4

T. Red
R. A green lantern
I. The moon
V. Pitfall Harry
I+. Rhode Island
A. A small laser beam

421 and 422 ANSWERS

5 OR 6

T. It ran out of gas
R. *Air Wolf*
I. Medusa
V. Twelve
I+. Fruit
A. Walt Disney

421 and 422 ANSWERS

1 OR 2

T. What is the name of the scientist/brain surgeon/rock star who leads the Hong Kong Cavaliers?(6)
R. On what TV show did John Travolta get his start by playing Vinny Barbarino?(3)
I. Which X-Man is Peter Rasputin?(5)
V. How many skipping ropes are used in Double Dutch?(2)
I+. Which planet has two moons named Phobos and Deimos?(1)
A. What is the robot arm on the Space Shuttle called?(4)

QUESTIONS 423 and 424

---

3 OR 4

T. Who was the star of *Saturday Night Fever* and its sequel, *Stayin' Alive*?(4)
R. In what TV soap opera did Christian LeBlanc play Kirk McColl?(6)
I. Who is Marvel Comics' Japanese superhero?(5)
V. Name the two major baseball leagues.(3)
I+. Which planet has the Great Red Spot?(1)
A. What is the name for a Russian space traveler?(2)

QUESTIONS 423 and 424

---

5 OR 6

T. Who were the two stars of *The Blue Lagoon*?(5)
R. In what TV soap opera did Michael Damian play Danny Romalotti?(6)
I. On what continent was the X-Man Storm born?(4)
V. What is the name of the games played by the top baseball team from each league to determine the year's best team?(3)
I+. Which planet was once thought to have canals on its surface?(1)
A. What is the name for an American space traveler?(2)

QUESTIONS 423 and 424

1 OR 2

T. Buckaroo Banzai
R. *Welcome Back Kotter*
I. Colossus
V. Two
I+. Mars
A. Canadarm

423 and 424 ANSWERS

3 OR 4

T. John Travolta
R. *All My Children*
I. Sunfire
V. The American League and the National League
I+. Jupiter
A. Cosmonaut

423 and 424 ANSWERS

5 OR 6

T. Brooke Shields and Christopher Atkins
R. *The Young and The Restless*
I. Africa
V. The World Series
I+. Mars
A. Astronaut

423 and 424 ANSWERS

1 OR 2

T. Who was the star of *Footloose*?(3)
R. In what TV soap opera did Larry Lau play Greg Nelson?(5)
I. What superhero group is made up of Bug, Marionette, Acroyear, Huntarr, Fireflyte, and Commander Rann?(6)
V. How many games must a team win to take the World Series?(4)
I+. Which known planet's orbit takes it the farthest away from the sun?(2)
A. What do you call a scientist who studies chemistry?(1)

QUESTIONS 425 and 426

3 OR 4

T. Who played Dallas in *The Outsiders*?(3)
R. In what TV series did Sue Ellen fell in love with a college student played by Chris Atkins?(6)
I. Where does Superman keep his Clark Kent clothes when he is in his Superman costume?(2)
V. In baseball, who stands behind the catcher and decides whether the pitches are balls or strikes?(2)
I+. Which planet is sometimes called the Evening Star?(1)
A. What do you call a scientist who studies the stars?(5)

QUESTIONS 425 and 426

5 OR 6

T. Who played Steve in *The Outsiders*?(4)
R. On *Diff'rent Strokes*, what was Arnold's brother's name?(2)
I. Which superhero's real name is Ralph Dibny?(5)
V. How many outs can a team get in baseball before it is retired?(3)
I+. Which planet is called the Red Planet?(1)
A. What does a paleontologist study?(6)

QUESTIONS 425 and 426

1 OR 2

T. Kevin Bacon
R. *All My Children*
I. The Mighty Micronauts
V. Four
I+. Pluto
A. Chemist

425 and 426 ANSWERS

3 OR 4

T. Matt Dillon
R. *Dallas*
I. In a pouch in his cape
V. The umpire
I+. Venus
A. An astronomer

425 and 426 ANSWERS

5 OR 6

T. Tom Cruise
R. Willis
I. The Elongated Man
V. Three
I+. Mars
A. Ancient life forms, like dinosaurs

425 and 426 ANSWERS

1 OR 2

T. Which member of *The Outsiders* wore a Mickey Mouse T-shirt?(4)
R. What comedian co-starred with E.T. on the little alien's first TV special?(2)
I. Which comic-book hero is known as The Caped Crusader?(1)
V. In what sport do the best teams win pennants?(5)
I+. Which planet is closer to the sun, Jupiter or Saturn?(6)
A. What kind of a scientist is Carl Sagan?(3)

QUESTIONS 431 and 432

3 OR 4

T. In which science-fiction movie did Sting play a character called Feyd?(5)
R. In which TV show did David Hasselhoff play a crime fighter?(2)
I. Which superhero's real name is Dinah Lance?(6)
V. How many strikes are you allowed in baseball before you're out?(1)
I+. Which planet is closer to the sun, Mars or Venus?(4)
A. What is the name of the French scientist who produces TV shows about his underwater work?(3)

QUESTIONS 431 and 432

5 OR 6

T. In what movie did Mr. T. play a taxi driver?(5)
R. In what soap opera did Steve Bond play Jimmy Lee Holt?(6)
I. Which superhero is known as The Tiny Titan?(4)
V. How many balls are allowed in baseball before the batter can walk?(1)
I+. How many planets are between Earth and the sun?(2)
A. With what kind of machine can you use a disk-drive?(3)

QUESTIONS 431 and 432

1 OR 2

T. Two-bit
R. Robin Williams
I. The Batman
V. Baseball
I+. Jupiter
A. Astronomer

431 and 432 ANSWERS

3 OR 4

T. *Dune*
R. *Knight Rider*
I. The Black Canary
V. Three
I+. Venus
A. Jacques Cousteau

431 and 432 ANSWERS

5 OR 6

T. *D.C. Cab*
R. *General Hospital*
I. The Atom
V. Four
I+. Two (Mercury and Venus)
A. A computer

431 and 432 ANSWERS

1 OR 2

T. Who starred with Paul McCartney in the video *Say Say Say*?(3)
R. In what TV soap opera did Grant Aleksander play Phillip Spaulding?(5)
I. Who is the Black Canary's boyfriend?(6)
V. How many innings are in a regular baseball game?(4)
I+. On what planet did the Viking robot space vehicle land?(1)
A. What part of a pencil makes the mark on paper?(2)

QUESTIONS 433 and 434

---

3 OR 4

T. Who played the role of Sodapop in *The Outsiders*?(6)
R. What character did Scott Baio play in the TV series *Happy Days*?(4)
I. What superhero's real name is Walter Langkowski?(5)
V. How many squares at a time may the King move in chess?(1)
I+. Which planet is the only one with a system of rings that can be seen through binoculars from Earth?(2)
A. What was the first theme park built by Walt Disney?(3)

QUESTIONS 433 and 434

---

5 OR 6

T. In which movie did Tom Cruise and Lea Thompson star?(6)
R. In which soap opera did John Stamos star?(4)
I. Which superhero is half human and half Kree?(3)
V. How many squares at a time may the Queen move in chess?(2)
I+. Which planet is sometimes called Earth's twin?(5)
A. What breakfast cereal comes in fruit flavors and is shaped like tiny doughnuts?(1)

QUESTIONS 433 and 434

1 OR 2

T. Michael Jackson
R. *Guiding Light*
I. Green Arrow
V. Nine (unless the score is tied)
I+. Mars
A. The lead

433 and 434 ANSWERS

3 OR 4

T. Rob Lowe
R. Chachi
I. Sasquatch
V. One
I+. Saturn
A. Disneyland

433 and 434 ANSWERS

5 OR 6

T. *All the Right Moves*
R. *General Hospital*
I. Ms. Marvel
V. As many as the player wants
I+. Venus
A. Froot Loops

433 and 434 ANSWERS

1 OR 2

T. In what movie did Balu the Bear sing "The Bare Necessities"?(3)
R. What TV show took place in the Manhattan High School for The Performing Arts?(1)
I. What superhero wears a costume that looks like the Canadian flag?(6)
V. What game is played on a diamond?(4)
I+. What are the dark areas of the moon called, even though there is no free water on the moon?(2)
A. Which Masters of the Universe character is able to spray water from its mouth?(5)

QUESTIONS 435 and 436

---

3 OR 4

T. In *Snow White and the Seven Dwarfs*, who was the only completely bald dwarf?(1)
R. In *Fame*, what character does Gene Anthony Ray play?(2)
I. Which superhero group is made up of Guardian, Sasquatch, Northstar, and Aurora?(5)
V. What is the only chess piece that can jump over other pieces?(3)
I+. Which planet has four main moons called Io, Europa, Ganymede, and Callisto?(6)
A. Who does Romeo Sprite kiss?(4)

QUESTIONS 435 and 436

---

5 OR 6

T. What puppet wanted to be a real boy?(1)
R. What TV show featured the characters Sabrina, Chris, and Kelly?(2)
I. In what country is Alpha Flight based?(6)
V. How many Bishops does each player have at the beginning of a game of chess?(4)
I+. What is the largest planet in our solar system?(5)
A. Which gang lives in Green Meadow?(3)

QUESTIONS 435 and 436

1 OR 2

T. *The Jungle Book*
R. *Fame*
I. The Guardian
V. Baseball
I+. Seas
A. Kobra Khan

435 and 436 ANSWERS

3 OR 4

T. Dopey
R. Leroy
I. Alpha Flight
V. The Knight
I+. Jupiter
A. Everyone!

435 and 436 ANSWERS

5 OR 6

T. Pinocchio
R. *Charlie's Angels*
I. Canada
V. Two
I+. Jupiter
A. The Get Along Gang

435 and 436 ANSWERS

1 OR 2

T. What singing insect was Pinocchio's "conscience"?(1)
R. Which Smurf is never happy?(3)
I. What humorous hero does Bobby Caswell turn into when he claps his hands?(5)
V. In American football, how many players can each team have on the field at one time?(4)
I·. What is a shorter name for a binary digit used in computers?(6)
A. What action figure toy is called A Real American Hero?(2)

QUESTIONS 441 and 442

3 OR 4

T. Who was carved out of wood by Gepetto?(6)
R. Which Smurf is always tripping and dropping things?(1)
I. What is the name of the Teenage Witch in *Archie* comics?(5)
V. In what sport is the ball called the pigskin?(2)
I·. In what city is the Statue of Liberty?(4)
A. What cereal does the shape-changing Chocle love?(3)

QUESTIONS 441 and 442

5 OR 6

T. What was Pinocchio before he became a boy?(1)
R. Which Smurf can build things?(2)
I. In *Archie* comics, what is the name of Josie's singing group?(6)
V. In American football, what is the championship game played by the top teams of the National Conference and the American Conference?(3)
I·. Which state is called the Aloha State?(4)
A. Whose castle is right in the middle of Disneyland?(5)

QUESTIONS 441 and 442

1 OR 2

T. Jiminy Cricket
R. Grouchy
I. Thunder Bunny
V. Eleven
I+. Bit (for *b*inary dig*it*)
A. G.I. Joe

441 and 442 ANSWERS

3 OR 4

T. Pinocchio
R. Clumsy
I. Sabrina
V. Football
I+. New York
A. Choco Crunch

441 and 442 ANSWERS

5 OR 6

T. A wooden puppet (marionette)
R. Handy
I. Josie and the Pussycats
V. The Superbowl
I+. Hawaii
A. Cinderella's

441 and 442 ANSWERS

1 OR 2

T. In the movie *Fantasia*, which animated character played the Sorcerer's Apprentice?(2)
R. Who is the only Smurf to have a beard?(1)
I. In *Archie* comics, what is the name of Alexandra's cat?(4)
V. How many points do you get for a touchdown in football?(3)
I+. How many states were there when the United States first became a nation?(6)
A. Which Care Bear has a heart on its tummy?(5)

QUESTIONS 443

3 OR 4

T. In the movie *Fantasia*, what did the Sorcerer's Apprentice magically make carry water to the well?(2)
R. What car was built by Knight Industries?(1)
I. In *Archie* comics, what does Alexandra's hair look like?(6)
V. How many yards do you need for a first down in football?(5)
I+. Which state is known as the Sunshine State?(3)
A. What is pictured on Cheer Bear's tummy?(4)

QUESTIONS 443

5 OR 6

T. Who had two mean stepsisters?(2)
R. Who was the Six Million Dollar Man?(6)
I. Who keeps his money in the money bin?(1)
V. In football, how many points do you get for a field goal?(5)
I+. In which state will you find the Grand Canyon?(4)
A. Which Care Bear has a rain cloud on its tummy?(3)

QUESTIONS 443

1 OR 2

T. Mickey Mouse
R. Papa Smurf
I. Sebastian
V. Six
I+. Thirteen
A. Tenderheart Bear

443 ANSWERS

3 OR 4

T. A broom
R. KITT
I. Black with one white streak
V. Ten
I+. Florida
A. A rainbow

443 ANSWERS

5 OR 6

T. Cinderella
R. Steve Austin (played by Lee Majors)
I. Uncle Scrooge McDuck
V. Three
I+. Arizona
A. Grumpy Bear

443 ANSWERS

1 OR 2

T. What was Cinderella's coach made from?(1)
R. What kind of woman was Jaime Sommers?(3)
I. Who is Prince Crystar's evil twin brother?(6)
V. Not including the end zones, how long is an American football field?(5)
I+. In which state is Hollywood?(2)
A. Which Care Bear has a birthday cake on its tummy?(4)

QUESTIONS 444

3 OR 4

T. At what time did Cinderella have to leave the ball?(1)
R. What did the Six Million Dollar Man do before he became bionic?(2)
I. What city does Prince Crystar rule?(6)
V. Name one of three interactive computer games that are played in the Great Underground Empire.(5)
I+. Which state is closer to the Pacific Ocean: North Carolina or North Dakota?(3)
A. Which Care Bear has a moon and stars on its tummy?(4)

QUESTIONS 444

5 OR 6

T. What did Cinderella leave behind at the ball?(1)
R. Who was the boss of the Six Million Dollar Man and the Bionic Woman?(2)
I. What are the colors of Aquaman's costume?(6)
V. How many minutes of game time are in each quarter of a football game?(5)
I+. Which state is closer to the Atlantic Ocean: Minnesota or Michigan?(3)
A. Which Care Bear has two smiling flowers on its tummy?(4)

QUESTIONS 444

1 OR 2

T. A pumpkin
R. The Bionic Woman
I. Prince Moltar
V. One hundred yards
I+. California
A. Birthday Bear

444 ANSWERS

---

3 OR 4

T. Midnight (or 12 o'clock)
R. He was an astronaut
I. Galax
V. *Zork I, Zork II, or Zork III*
I+. North Dakota
A. Bedtime Bear

444 ANSWERS

---

5 OR 6

T. A glass slipper
R. Oscar (Goldman)
I. Orange and green
V. Fifteen minutes
I+. Michigan
A. Friend Bear

444 ANSWERS

1 OR 2

T. In what movie did the Fairy Godmother sing "Bibbidi-Bobbidi-Boo"?(2)
R. In the TV series *M*A*S*H*, what was the occupation of Hawkeye and Trapper John?(1)
I. What is the name of Prince Crystar's uncle?(4)
V. What sport is played with bats and wickets?(6)
I+. Of which state is Denver the capital?(3)
A. What is the name of Strawberry Shortcake's cat?(5)

QUESTIONS 445 and 446

3 OR 4

T. What was the name of the tiny magical creature that flew around with Peter Pan?(3)
R. What flew through the air at the beginning of each *M*A*S*H* show?(1)
I. What is the name of the wizard who transformed Prince Crystar into a Crystal Warrior?(5)
V. What is the national sport of Canada?(D)
I+. Of which state is Phoenix the capital?(2)
A. What are the names of Strawberry Shortcake's twin friends who have a dog named Sugar Woofer?(4)

QUESTIONS 445 and 446

5 OR 6

T. Who was the pirate who wanted to kill Peter Pan?(2)
R. Name one of the two commanding officers in the *M*A*S*H* TV show.(4)
I. On what world does Prince Crystar have his adventures?(5)
V. What is the national sport of the United States?(1)
I+. What is the name for the system of measurement that uses meters, kilograms, and Celsius degrees?(6)
A. Which friend of Strawberry Shortcake has a pet named Marza Panda?(3)

QUESTIONS 445 and 446

1 OR 2

T. *Cinderella*
R. They were doctors (surgeons)
I. Uncle Feldspar
V. Cricket
I+. Colorado
A. Custard

445 and 446 ANSWERS

3 OR 4

T. Tinkerbell
R. Helicopters
I. Ogeode
V. Lacrosse
I+. Arizona
A. Lem and Ada

445 and 446 ANSWERS

5 OR 6

T. Captain Hook
R. Colonel Blake or Colonel Potter
I. Crystalium
V. Baseball
I+. Metric system (also called S.I.)
A. Almond Tea

445 and 446 ANSWERS

1 OR 2

T. What was Peter Pan's nickname for Tinkerbell?(2)
R. Who was the Chief Engineer in *Star Trek*?(1)
I. Which superhero group do Sunspot and Cannonball belong to?(4)
V. What is the national sport of Japan?(5)
I+. How many ounces in a pound?(3)
A. What kind of toys are Clawgut, Ripsaw, and Voltor?(6)

QUESTIONS 451 and 452

---

3 OR 4

T. In *Peter Pan*, how did Captain Hook lose his hand?(2)
R. Who was the Science Officer in *Star Trek*?(1)
I. Name two superhero groups that are based in Professor Xavier's School for Gifted Youngsters.(4)
V. How many holes make up a standard round of golf?(3)
I+. How many feet in a mile?(5)
A. Which friend of Strawberry Shortcake has a pet named Marmalade?(6)

QUESTIONS 451 and 452

---

5 OR 6

T. In *Peter Pan*, what sound warned Captain Hook that the crocodile was coming?(4)
R. Who was the Communications Officer in *Star Trek*?(3)
I. In the New Mutants, what can Rahne Sinclair turn into?(5)
V. What is the name for a person who carries a golfer's clubs?(1)
I+. What kind of plug makes gasoline burn in a car engine?(6)
A. Where does Strawberry Shortcake live?(2)

QUESTIONS 451 and 452

1 OR 2

T. Tink
R. Scotty
I. The New Mutants
V. Baseball
I·. Sixteen
A. Starriors

451 and 452 ANSWERS

3 OR 4

T. A crocodile bit it off
R. Mr. Spock
I. The X-Men and the New Mutants
V. Eighteen
I·. 5,280
A. Orange Blossom

451 and 452 ANSWERS

5 OR 6

T. The ticking of an alarm clock
R. Lieutenant Uhura
I. A wolf
V. A caddy
I·. A spark plug
A. Strawberryland

451 and 452 ANSWERS

1 OR 2

T. In the movie *Supergirl*, how were Supergirl and Superman related?(2)
R. In what TV series was there a car called *General Lee*?(4)
I. What color is the Green Lantern's mask?(3)
V. How many divisions are in the NHL?(6)
I+. Does a hovercraft fly over land, water, or both?(5)
A. What kind of doll comes with a birth certificate and adoption papers?(1)

QUESTIONS 453 and 454

3 OR 4

T. In the movie *Supergirl*, what was Supergirl's Kryptonian name?(5)
R. What kind of car was *General Lee*?(D)
I. What color are the Green Lantern's boots?(2)
V. What do the initials NHL stand for?(1)
I+. Does a comet's tail point toward the sun or away from it?(4)
A. What is the name of Barbie's boyfriend?(3)

QUESTIONS 453 and 454

5 OR 6

T. In the movie *Supergirl*, what was Supergirl's secret identity?(3)
R. In *The Dukes of Hazzard*, what was Hogg's nickname?(2)
I. What color are Flash's boots?(5)
V. What comes from Wykoosa Valley?(4)
I+. Other than our own, what is the only other galaxy that can be seen from the United States?(6)
A. What's the name of the toy kit that lets you stick all sorts of face parts on a potato?(1)

QUESTIONS 453 and 454

1 OR 2

T. They were cousins
R. *The Dukes of Hazzard*
I. Green
V. Four
I+. Both
A. A Cabbage Patch Kid

453 and 454 ANSWERS

---

3 OR 4

T. Kara
R. A Dodge Charger
I. Green
V. National Hockey League
I+. Away from it
A. Ken

453 and 454 ANSWERS

---

5 OR 6

T. Linda Lee Danvers
R. Boss
I. Yellow
V. Koosas
I+. Andromeda
A. Mr. Potato Head

453 and 454 ANSWERS

1 OR 2

T. In the movie *Supergirl*, what was the name of the Kryptonian city that floated in space?(4)
R. In what TV show did the kids hang out at Arnold's Drive-in?(1)
I. What is the name of the intergalactic organization that all the Green Lanterns of the galaxy belong to?(5)
V. What do the initials AFL stand for?(6)
I·. Who became President after Jimmy Carter?(2)
A. What kind of toys are Trapper Tom, Ranger Rick, and Jumper Joe?(3)

QUESTIONS 455 and 456

3 OR 4

T. What kind of imaginary creature was featured in the movie *Splash*?(2)
R. Which character on *Happy Days* fell in love with Pinky Tuscadero?(5)
I. Who is Superman's best friend?(1)
V. In what sport is the championship determined by playoffs between the top teams of the Campbell Conference and the Wales Conference?(6)
I·. What is the capital of Missouri?(4)
A. What kind of doll looks like a big green worm and has a face that glows if you hug it?(3)

QUESTIONS 455 and 456

5 OR 6

T. In the movie *Iceman*, what do the scientists nickname the caveman?(3)
R. On *Happy Days*, what was Richie's sister's name?(4)
I. What does Superman use to lock and unlock his Fortress of Solitude?(6)
V. In hockey, how many players can each team have on the ice at one time?(5)
I·. Which of the United States is farthest north?(1)
A. What kind of action figures must face the evil agents of Cobra?(2)

QUESTIONS 455 and 456

1 OR 2

T. Argo City
R. *Happy Days*
I. The Green Lantern Corps
V. American Football League
I+. Ronald Reagan
A. Li'l Loggers

455 and 456 ANSWERS

3 OR 4

T. A mermaid
R. Fonzie
I. Jimmy Olsen
V. Hockey
I+. St. Louis
A. Glo Worm

455 and 456 ANSWERS

5 OR 6

T. Charlie
R. Joanie
I. An airplane direction-marker
V. Six
I+. Alaska
A. G.I. Joe

455 and 456 ANSWERS

1 OR 2

T. In the movie *Greystoke*, by what other name was Lord Greystoke known?(1)
R. On the show *Fraggle Rock*, where do the Doozers live?(3)
I. How was green kryptonite formed?(4)
V. How many periods are in a hockey game?(5)
I+. Name the two main political parties in the United States.(2)
A. What is the name of G.I. Joe's helicopter?(6)

QUESTIONS 461 and 462

---

3 OR 4

T. What did the Muppets try to do in *The Muppets Take Manhattan*?(4)
R. On the show *Fraggle Rock*, what is the name for the things that the Doozers build?(3)
I. How often can a piece of red kryptonite affect Superman?(5)
V. How many minutes of game time are in each period of a hockey game?(6)
I+. If you rang a bell where there was no air, would the bell make a louder noise than usual or no noise?(1)
A. What action figure has a Skystriker combat jet?(2)

QUESTIONS 461 and 462

---

5 OR 6

T. In *The Ice Pirates*, what did the pirates try to steal from the other spaceships? (And you can't say "Ice"!)(5)
R. On the show *Fraggle Rock*, who is the King of the Universe?(1)
I. What would gold kryptonite do to Superman?(6)
V. In basketball, how many players can each team have on the court at one time?(3)
I+. What is the capital of New Mexico?(4)
A. What do you pump into an Air Jammer Car to make it go?(2)

QUESTIONS 461 and 462

1 OR 2

T. Tarzan
R. In Fraggle Rock
I. Bits of Superman's home planet passed through a mysterious green cloud in space
V. Three
I+. The Democrats and the Republicans
A. *Dragonfly*

3 OR 4

T. Put on a musical show (on Broadway)
R. Doozer Constructions
I. Just once
V. Twenty
I+. No noise
A. G.I. Joe

461 and 462 ANSWERS

5 OR 6

T. Water
R. Daddy Gorg
I. It would take away his powers forever
V. Five
I+. Santa Fe
A. Air

461 and 462 ANSWERS

1 OR 2

T. In the movie *Gremlins*, which Walt Disney movie did the gremlins watch?(1)

R. In what show does Uncle Galilo invent things that work underwater?(2)

I. What is the name of the vehicle on which Batgirl travels?(3)

V. Name one of the two sports in which a ball can be dribbled.(4)

I+. What is the highest mountain in the United States?(6)

A. What Masters of the Universe playset comes with an Echo Microphone?(5)

QUESTIONS 463 and 464

---

3 OR 4

T. What is the title of the second movie about Conan?(3)

R. Which Fraggle wears a pop-can tab on a chain around her neck?(4)

I. Which superhero is known as the Man of Tomorrow?(5)

V. How many players are on the court during a doubles match in tennis?(2)

I+. What is the boiling point of water in Fahrenheit degrees?(6)

A. Which toy company makes Hot Wheels?(1)

QUESTIONS 463 and 464

---

5 OR 6

T. In the movie *Iceman*, where was the frozen caveman found?(3)

R. Which Fraggle gets postcards from his uncle, Travelling Matt?(2)

I. Where did the indestructible cloth of Superman's costume come from?(5)

V. In what sport are you allowed to carry a maximum of fourteen clubs?(1)

I+. Who was the first woman Vice Presidential candidate of a major U.S. political party?(4)

A. How many color squares are there on a Rubik's Cube?(6)

QUESTIONS 463 and 464

1 OR 2

T. *Snow White and the Seven Dwarfs*
R. *Snorks*
I. The Batcycle
V. Basketball or soccer
I+. Mount McKinley
A. *Snake Mountain*

463 and 464 ANSWERS

3 OR 4

T. *Conan the Destroyer*
R. Mokey
I. Superman
V. Four
I+. 212°
A. Mattel

463 and 464 ANSWERS

5 OR 6

T. The North Pole (Arctic)
R. Gobo
I. They were his baby blankets from his home planet
V. Golf
I+. Geraldine Ferraro
A. Fifty-four

463 and 464 ANSWERS

1 OR 2

T. In *Return of the Jedi*, who freed Han Solo from the carbonite?(1)
R. Which Fraggle wears a hat pulled down over his eyes?(4)
I. What were the names of Superman's Kryptonite parents?(5)
V. By at least how many points must you win a game of tennis?(2)
I+. What is the capital of Massachusetts?(3)
A. What provides the heat in an Easy-Bake Oven?(6)

QUESTIONS 465 and 466

---

3 OR 4

T. In *Return of the Jedi*, what character did Billy Dee Williams play?(1)
R. Which Fraggle wears her hair in two ponytails?(5)
I. What were the names of Superman's Earth parents?(4)
V. By at least how many points must you win a game of Ping-Pong?(3)
I+. In which direction does a compass usually point?(2)
A. Which toy company makes the Big Wheel tricycle?(6)

QUESTIONS 465 and 466

---

5 OR 6

T. In *The Empire Strikes Back*, Yoda said there was "another." In *Return of the Jedi*, who was the "other" he meant?(1)
R. Which Fraggle can never make up his mind?(3)
I. On *Diff'rent Strokes*, what was the name of Arnold's adoptive father?(2)
V. In baseball, what is the name of the playing position between second and third base?(5)
I+. What is the second largest country in the world?(4)
A. What two accessories come with the Yoda action figure?(6)

QUESTIONS 465 and 466

1 OR 2

T. Leia
R. Boober
I. Lara and Jor-el
V. Two
I+. Boston
A. A light bulb

465 and 466 ANSWERS

3 OR 4

T. Lando Calrissian
R. Red
I. Jonathan and Martha Kent
V. Two
I+. North
A. Marx

465 and 466 ANSWERS

5 OR 6

T. Leia
R. Wembly
I. Philip Drummond
V. Shortstop
I+. Canada
A. His Gimer Stick (cane) and a snake

465 and 466 ANSWERS

1 OR 2

T. What animals were featured in *Lady and The Tramp*?(2)
R. What is Chip's and Dale's favorite kind of nut?(4)
I. What comic-book hero does the Joker usually fight?(1)
V. In *Basic Dungeons and Dragons*, from which three alignments may you choose for your player character?(3)
I+. What country do the initials U.K. stand for?(6)
A. What is the name of the device that lets a computer "talk" to other computers on the telephone?(5)

QUESTIONS 511 and 512

---

3 OR 4

T. What animated movie featured the three Good Fairies: Flora, Fauna, and Merriweather?(6)
R. What kind of animal are Chip and Dale?(1)
I. What superhero does Loki, God of Mischief, usually fight?(4)
V. To roll up a Thief's hit points in *Dungeons and Dragons*, how many sides should the die have?(2)
I+. What is the basic unit of money used in England?(5)
A. Which company makes the Macintosh personal computer?(3)

QUESTIONS 511 and 512

---

5 OR 6

T. In what animated film did the evil Cruella de Vil kidnap a vast number of Dalmation puppies?(3)
R. Who is the bad-tempered duck that often fights with Chip and Dale?(2)
I. What superhero does the Riddler usually fight?(1)
V. In *Basic Dungeons and Dragons*, which character class cannot use edged weapons?(4)
I+. What is a more common name for the star Polaris?(6)
A. What are PASCAL, LOGO, and FORTH?(5)

QUESTIONS 511 and 512

1 OR 2

T. Dogs
R. Acorn
I. The Batman
V. Lawful, Chaotic, or Neutral
I+. United Kingdom
A. Modem

511 and 512 ANSWERS

3 OR 4

T. *Sleeping Beauty*
R. Chipmunks
I. The Mighty Thor
V. Four
I+. The pound (Sterling)
A. Apple

511 and 512 ANSWERS

5 OR 6

T. *One Hundred and One Dalmations*
R. Donald Duck
I. The Batman
V. Clerics
I+. The North Star
A. Programming languages for computers

511 and 512 ANSWERS

1 OR 2

T. Which king had his story told in the animated movie *The Sword and the Stone*?(3)
R. What color is Donald Duck's bow tie?(2)
I. What superhero group does Colossus's sister belong to?(6)
V. In *Basic Dungeons and Dragons*, which two character classes have infravision?(4)
I+. How many sides does a pentagon have?(1)
A. What command do you type into a computer to make it run a Basic program?(5)

QUESTIONS 513 and 514

3 OR 4

T. In *The Sword and the Stone*, what was the name of the magician who taught the young boy?(2)
R. What color is Donald Duck's hat?(1)
I. What color is Wonder Woman's headband?(5)
V. To roll up hit points for a fighter in *Dungeons and Dragons*, how many sides should the die have?(4)
I+. How many sides does an octagon have?(3)
A. In Basic programming, what does a computer do when it comes to a command beginning with "REM"?(6)

QUESTIONS 513 and 514

5 OR 6

T. In *The Sword and the Stone*, what did it mean if you could pull the sword from the stone?(1)
R. What color is Daisy Duck's bow?(4)
I. What superhero group do Hawkman and Hawkgirl belong to?(5)
V. In *Basic Dungeons and Dragons*, what is the only character class that can "turn the undead"?(6)
I+. How many surfaces does a cone have?(2)
A. What happens to a computer program in RAM when the power is turned off?(3)

QUESTIONS 513 and 514

1 OR 2

T. King Arthur
R. Red
I. The New Mutants
V. Elves and Dwarfs
I+. Five
A. RUN

513 and 514 ANSWERS

---

3 OR 4

T. Merlin
R. Blue
I. Gold (or yellow)
V. Eight
I+. Eight
A. The computer ignores it and goes on

513 and 514 ANSWERS

---

5 OR 6

T. You would be king
R. Pink
I. The Justice League of America
V. Clerics
I+. Two
A. The program is lost

513 and 514 ANSWERS

1 OR 2

T. In *The Sword and the Stone*, what was Mad Madam Mim's favorite color?(2)
R. Where does Donald Duck's Grandma live?(4)
I. Which comic-book hero decided to become a crimefighter because, as a child, he saw his parents murdered?(1)
V. In *Basic Dungeons and Dragons*, what is the maximum number of experience levels an Elf may advance?(5)
I+. Which of the Great Lakes is completely in the United States?(6)
A. Which company makes the TRS-80 computer?(3)

QUESTIONS 515 and 516

---

3 OR 4

T. In *The Jungle Book*, what kind of animal was Shere Khan?(1)
R. What is the name of the goose who helps Donald Duck's Grandma?(6)
I. Where were the Fantastic Four when they developed their super powers?(3)
V. Name any four of the six abilities rolled for when creating a player character for *Dungeons and Dragons.*(5)
I+. What is the name of the little bay at the south end of Hudson Bay?(4)
A. What kind of cookie has a note on a piece of paper inside it?(2)

QUESTIONS 515 and 516

---

5 OR 6

T. In *The Jungle Book*, what was the name of the little boy who was raised by Baloo the Bear?(4)
R. How many fingers, counting thumbs, does Mickey Mouse have?(3)
I. Who is the leader of the Fantastic Four?(5)
V. In *Dungeons and Dragons*, against what kind of an attack do you use a saving throw?(6)
I+. Which country is shaped like a boot?(2)
A. Who fell down and broke his crown?(1)

QUESTIONS 515 and 516

1 OR 2

T. Pink
R. On a farm
I. The Batman
V. Ten
I+. Lake Michigan
A. Radio Shack

515 and 516 ANSWERS

---

3 OR 4

T. A tiger
R. Gus
I. In a spaceship
V. Strength, Intelligence, Wisdom, Dexterity, Constitution, Charisma
I+. James Bay
A. A fortune cookie

515 and 516 ANSWERS

---

5 OR 6

T. Mowgli
R. Eight
I. Mr. Fantastic
V. A magic attack
I+. Italy
A. Jack

515 and 516 ANSWERS

1 OR 2

T. How many kittens did Duchess have to take care of in the animated movie *The Aristocats*?(2)
R. What was the first little pig's house made of?(1)
I. Name two of the Invisible Girl's superpowers.(3)
V. In *Dungeons and Dragons*, which one of these is not a first-level spell: Floating Disc, Sleep, Levitate, or Magic Missile?(4)
I+. If you are standing akimbo, where are your hands?(6)
A. What was Goofy's name before he was called Goofy?(5)

QUESTIONS 521 and 522

3 OR 4

T. In *Winnie-the-Pooh and the Honey Tree*, what did Pooh disguise himself as, in order to sneak up on the bees in the tree?(2)
R. What was the second little pig's house made of?(1)
I. How many circles are on the front of the Mighty Thor's costume?(4)
V. In *Dungeons and Dragons*, what do the initials DM stand for?(3)
I+. Does a barometer measure air pressure or light intensity?(6)
A. What was the title of the first Mickey Mouse cartoon to be publicly shown?(5)

QUESTIONS 521 and 522

5 OR 6

T. What was the name of Winnie-the-Pooh's little pig friend?(2)
R. What was the third little pig's house made of?(1)
I. In *Superman* comics, what kind of creature is Lori Lemaris?(3)
V. In *Dungeons and Dragons*, what do the initials NPC stand for?(4)
I+. What part of the body varies the most between alligators and crocodiles?(6)
A. How long does a C-60 cassette tape play?(5)

QUESTIONS 521 and 522

1 OR 2

T. Three
R. Straw
I. She can make herself invisible; she can make other objects invisible; she can project invisible force fields
V. Levitate
I+. On your hips
A. Dippy Dawg

3 OR 4

T. A little black raincloud
R. Wood
I. Six
V. Dungeon Master
I+. Air pressure
A. *Steamboat Willie*

5 OR 6

T. Piglet
R. Brick
I. A mermaid
V. Non-Player Character
I+. The head (Alligators have shorter, wider heads)
A. Sixty minutes

---

1 OR 2

T. What was the name of the little boy who played with Winnie-the-Pooh?(2)
R. Who said "I'll huff and I'll puff and I'll bloooow your house down"?(1)
I. In *Superman* comics, what city is Lori Lemaris from?(5)
V. In *Dungeons and Dragons*, what is the player who communicates with the Dungeon Master called?(4)
I+. What is the first letter in the Greek alphabet?(3)
A. How many grooves does a standard record have on one side?(D)

QUESTIONS 523 and 524

---

3 OR 4

T. In *Winnie-the-Pooh and the Blustery Day*, who had a tail with a pink bow on it?(2)
R. What did the Three Little Pigs say when the Wolf said "Let me in"?(1)
I. What is Clark Kent's job?(5)
V. In *Dungeons and Dragons*, what is the player who maps the dungeon called?(4)
I+. Who are Prince William of Wales's parents?(6)
A. Which cereal is the Breakfast of Champions?(3)

QUESTIONS 523 and 524

---

5 OR 6

T. In *Winnie-the-Pooh and the Blustery Day*, who was very, very bouncy?(2)
R. Which of the Three Little Pigs' houses couldn't the Wolf blow down?(1)
I. What TV station does Clark Kent work for?(6)
V. In *Dungeons and Dragons*, how many minutes of game time make up each regular move?(5)
I+. What two letters show that a time is *before* noon?(3)
A. Which chocolate bar is advertised as "chocolate-covered nothing"?(4)

QUESTIONS 523 and 524

---

1 OR 2

T. Christopher Robin
R. The Big Bad Wolf
I. Atlantis
V. The Caller
I+. Alpha
A. One

523 and 524 ANSWERS

3 OR 4

T. Eeyore
R. "Not by the hair on our chinny-chin-chins"
I. TV newscaster
V. The Mapper
I+. Charles and Diana, the Prince and Princess of Wales
A. Wheaties

523 and 524 ANSWERS

5 OR 6

T. Tigger
R. Practical Pig's brick house (The third one)
I. WGBS
V. Ten
I+. *a.m.*
A. Aero Bar

523 and 524 ANSWERS

1 OR 2

T. In Walt Disney's *Robin Hood*, what kind of animal was Robin?(6)

R. What was Goofy's sports program called?(1)

I. In *Garfield the Cat* cartoons, how many spots does Odie the dog have?(5)

V. On what kind of vehicle would you perform a trick called a front brake endo X-up?(2)

I+. What two letters show that a time is *after* noon?(3)

A. What is the name of the hospital where Cabbage Patch Kids are born?(4)

QUESTIONS 525 and 526

3 OR 4

T. In Walt Disney's *Robin Hood*, what kind of animal was Maid Marian?(5)

R. What color are Mickey Mouse's shorts?(1)

I. What is the name of Aquaman's sidekick?(2)

V. In the video game *Phoenix*, what happens if you destroy all of the warbirds that defend the mothership?(3)

I+. What can't you do if you have amnesia?(4)

A. What do Americans call the thing that British people call a lift?(6)

QUESTIONS 525 and 526

5 OR 6

T. In Walt Disney's *Robin Hood*, what kind of animal was Prince John?(5)

R. On *Sesame Street*, what color is Grover?(2)

I. What is the name of Supergirl's supercat?(4)

V. In the video game *Defender*, what button can you press if you're surrounded and have no more bombs?(3)

I+. In what two environments do amphibians live?(1)

A. What name is written on the bottom of each Cabbage Patch Kid?(D)

QUESTIONS 525 and 526

1 OR 2

T. A fox
R. Sport Goofy
I. Two (one on each side)
V. Bicycle (BMX)
I+. *p.m.*
A. Babyland General

525 and 526 ANSWERS

3 OR 4

T. A fox
R. Red
I. Aqualad
V. A whole new group appears
I+. Remember
A. Elevator

525 and 526 ANSWERS

5 OR 6

T. A lion
R. Blue
I. Streaky
V. The hyperspace button
I+. Land and water
A. Xavier Roberts

525 and 526 ANSWERS

1 OR 2

T. In *20,000 Leagues Under the Sea*, did the 20,000 leagues mean the depth the submarine could reach, or the distance it could travel underwater?(2)
R. On *Sesame Street*, what color is Bert?(3)
I. Which superhero does the Sandman usually fight?(6)
V. In the game *Hungry, Hungry Hippos*, what do the hippos eat?(5)
I+. What is the name of our galaxy?(1)
A. On what part of your body would you wear a fez?(4)

QUESTIONS 531 and 532

3 OR 4

T. In *20,000 Leagues Under the Sea*, what was the name of the submarine?(4)
R. On *Sesame Street*, what color is Ernie?
I. Which superhero does the Hobgoblin usually fight?(5)
V. How many dice do you roll out of the cup in *Yahtzee*?(6)
I+. What is another name for the Aurora Borealis?(3)
A. What is the name for the carved pumpkin displayed on Halloween?(1)

QUESTIONS 531 and 532

5 OR 6

T. In *20,000 Leagues Under the Sea*, who was the captain of the submarine?(4)
R. On *Sesame Street*, who is taller: Ernie or Bert?(2)
I. Which superhero does Terra-man usually fight?(5)
V. What is the more difficult version of the game called *Perfection*?(6)
I+. What month is named for the Latin word for "nine"?(3)
A. What month is named for the two-faced Roman God, Janus?(1)

QUESTIONS 531 and 532

1 OR 2

T. The distance it could travel underwater
R. Yellow
I. Spider-man
V. Marbles
I+. The Milky Way
A. Your head (It's a hat)

531 and 532 ANSWERS

3 OR 4

T. The *Nautilus*
R. Orange
I. Spider-man
V. Five
I+. The Northern Lights
A. Jack-o'-lantern

531 and 532 ANSWERS

5 OR 6

T. Captain Nemo
R. Bert
I. Superman
V. *Super-Perfection*
I+. November (It was the ninth month in the early Roman calendar)
A. January

531 and 532 ANSWERS

1 OR 2

T. In *20,000 Leagues Under the Sea*, what kind of giant sea creature attacked the submarine?(1)
R. On *Sesame Street*, what color is Oscar?(2)
I. Who replaced the Thing as a member of the Fantastic Four?(4)
V. In what game do you try to remove the patient's funnybone without setting off the buzzer?(3)
I+. How many distinct colors are in a rainbow?(5)
A. What is the common name for equipment used for radio detecting and ranging?(6)

QUESTIONS 533 and 534

3 OR 4

T. What kind of car was Herbie, the Love Bug?(2)
R. On *Sesame Street*, who is known as The Grouch?(1)
I. What superhero does the Vulture usually fight?(3)
V. How many dice do you use in the board-game version of *Zaxxon*?(4)
I+. In what part of your body is the retina?(5)
A. What is the name for a male sheep?(6)

QUESTIONS 533 and 534

5 OR 6

T. In *Mary Poppins*, what did people do to make themselves float?(4)
R. On *Sesame Street*, what color is Big Bird?(1)
I. What symbol is on the front of Spider-man's costume?(2)
V. Which direction do you go when you stop on a snake tail in *Snakes and Ladders*?(3)
I+. What do you get when iron oxidizes?(6)
A. In TV commercials, how does America spell Relief?(5)

QUESTIONS 533 and 534

1 OR 2

T. A squid
R. Green
I. She-Hulk
V. *Operation*
I+. Seven (Red, orange, yellow, green, blue, indigo, and violet)
A. Radar

533 and 534 ANSWERS

---

3 OR 4

T. A Volkswagen Beetle (Bug)
R. Oscar
I. Spider-man
V. Two
I+. The eye
A. A ram

533 and 534 ANSWERS

---

5 OR 6

T. Laugh
R. Yellow
I. A spider
V. Down
I+. Rust
A. R-O-L-A-I-D-S

533 and 534 ANSWERS

1 OR 2

T. What was the name of the dog that couldn't follow the children in *Peter Pan*?(6)
R. Who used to be on *Sesame Street*, and then became host of *The Muppet Show*?(1)
I. What is Doonesbury's first name?(4)
V. What do you have to land on to go up in *Snakes and Ladders*?(2)
I+. Is an acute angle greater or less than 90°?(3)
A. What kind of vehicle would you find in a roundhouse?(5)

QUESTIONS 535 and 536

---

3 OR 4

T. What color were Peter Pan's clothes?(2)
R. Where did *The Muppet Show* take place?(3)
I. Which superhero flies in a glass airplane?(1)
V. What piece must you capture to end a game of *Stratego*?(4)
I+. What is the name for the layer of air that lies between the surface of the Earth and outer space?(6)
A. What British Earl is supposed to have invented the sandwich?(5)

QUESTIONS 535 and 536

---

5 OR 6

T. In *Peter Pan*, what color was Captain Hook's coat?(1)
R. On *The Muppet Show*, whose uncle owned the theater?(2)
I. Which two members of the Fantastic Four are married to each other?(5)
V. How many lakes are on a *Stratego* board?(4)
I+. Which Roman Emperor named the month of August after himself?(6)
A. Which day was named after Saturn, the Roman god of farming?(3)

QUESTIONS 535 and 536

1 OR 2

T. Nana
R. Kermit the Frog
I. Mike
V. The bottom of a ladder
I+. Less
A. A train

3 OR 4

T. Green
R. The Muppet Theater
I. Wonder Woman
V. The flag
I+. The atmosphere
A. The Earl of Sandwich

5 OR 6

T. Red
R. Scooter's
I. The Invisible Girl and Mr. Fantastic
V. Two
I+. Augustus
A. Saturday

1 OR 2

T. In *Return of the Jedi*, who threw the Emperor over the edge of the guard rail?(1)
R. On *The Muppet Show*, what was the Eagle's name?(3)
I. By what name is Prince Namor of Atlantis better known?(5)
V. In *Stratego*, what is the only piece that can defuse a bomb?(4)
I+. Is a sea horse a mammal or a fish?(2)
A. What kind of a person would carry a sceptre?(6)

QUESTIONS 541 and 542

---

3 OR 4

T. In *Return of the Jedi*, where was the Ewoks' village built?(2)
R. On *The Muppet Show*, what was Beauregard's job?(3)
I. What comic-book hero flies upon a silver surfboard?(1)
V. In *Stratego*, what are the only three pieces that can kill a Marshall?(5)
I+. How many seconds in three minutes?(4)
A. If you were using a seine, what would you be catching?(6)

QUESTIONS 541 and 542

---

5 OR 6

T. In *Return of the Jedi*, what had Luke Skywalker finally become?(3)
R. Who gave the cooking lessons on *The Muppet Show*?(1)
I. What superpower does Superman use to see things at a distance?(2)
V. What is the only *Stratego* piece that can move more than one square at a time?(5)
I+. How many seconds are in half a minute? (4)
A. Which friend of Strawberry Shortcake has a pet named Jelly Bear?(6)

QUESTIONS 541 and 542

1 OR 2

T. Darth Vader
R. Sam
I. The Sub-mariner
V. Miner
I+. A fish
A. A king or a queen

541 and 542 ANSWERS

3 OR 4

T. In the trees
R. He was the janitor
I. The Silver Surfer
V. The Spy, a bomb, or another Marshall
I+. 180
A. Fish (It's a net)

541 and 542 ANSWERS

5 OR 6

T. A Jedi Knight
R. The Swedish Chef
I. Telescopic vision
V. The Scout
I+. Thirty
A. Butter Cookie

541 and 542 ANSWERS

1 OR 2

T. Who grew up to be a giant at the end of *The Muppet Movie*?(2)
R. What was the title of the first T.V. movie made by Lucasfilm?(1)
I. Who did Alec Holland turn into when he was left for dead in the swamp?(3)
V. In what video game do you follow Bounty Bob and Yukon Yohan into an abandoned uranium mine?(6)
I+. What kind of a doctor is a pediatrician?(5)
A. What company did Nolan Bushnell first start?(4)

QUESTIONS 543 and 544

---

3 OR 4

T. What was the title of the Walt Disney film that featured the robots Bob, Vincent, and Maximillian?(2)
R. Name the robot on *Riptide*.(3)
I. Which superhero usually fights Kraven the Hunter?(1)
V. What do the fruits do in the video game *Ms. Pac-Man* that they don't do in *Pac-Man*?(4)
I+. What kind of a doctor is a podiatrist?(6)
A. For what company does Lee Iaccoca work?(5)

QUESTIONS 543 and 544

---

5 OR 6

T. In *The Empire Strikes Back*, who did Leia kiss first: Han or Luke?(2)
R. What color is the Incredible Hulk?(1)
I. Which superhero's mother is Queen Hippolyta?(4)
V. How many cities do you have in the arcade version of *Missile Command*?(5)
I+. Where on a house would you find shingles?(3)
A. What computer did Steve Wozniak help develop?(6)

QUESTIONS 543 and 544

1 OR 2

T. Animal
R. The Ewok Adventure
I. The Swamp Thing
V. *Miner 2049er*
I+. One who specializes in the care of babies and children
A. Atari

543 and 544 ANSWERS

3 OR 4

T. *The Black Hole*
R. Roboz
I. Spider-man
V. They move
I+. One who specializes in the care of feet
A. Chrysler

543 and 544 ANSWERS

5 OR 6

T. Luke
R. Green
I. Wonder Woman
V. Three
I+. The roof
A. The Apple (and the Macintosh and the Lisa)

543 and 544 ANSWERS

1 OR 2

T. In the *Star Wars* movies, one type of Imperial spaceship was called a T.I.E. Fighter. What did the initials stand for?(D)

R. In what TV show did the heroes have to fight the evil aliens called Draconians?(2)

I. Which superhero group is the Vision a member of?(4)

V. In the video game, what does Frogger have to cross before he can cross the river?(1)

I+. Where does silk come from?(3)

A. What kind of computer games is Scott Adams noted for designing?(5)

QUESTIONS 545 and 546

---

3 OR 4

T. In the movie *Tron*, what did the initials MCP stand for?(2)

R. On *Buck Rogers*, what color was Twiki?(1)

I. Which superhero group does Starfox belong to?(4)

V. On what part of your body would you wear Top-siders?(3)

I+. What's a shorter way of saying Self-contained Underwater Breathing Apparatus, when talking about deep-sea diving?(5)

A. What game is Gary Gygax noted for developing?(6)

QUESTIONS 545 and 546

---

5 OR 6

T. What is the episode title of the first *Star Wars* film?(5)

R. What green superhero did Lou Ferrigno play on television?(4)

I. By what names are the mutants Wanda and Pietro better known?(3)

V. In the Colecovision game, *Rescue in Gargamel's Castle*, who is being rescued?(1)

I+. From what two words is the word "smog" made?(6)

A. How do you use The Joyboard with video games?(2)

QUESTIONS 545 and 546

1 OR 2

T. Twin Ion Engine
R. *Buck Rogers*
I. The Avengers
V. The road
I+. Silkworms
A. Adventure (or interactive) games

545 and 546 ANSWERS

3 OR 4

T. Master Control Program
R. Gray (or silver)
I. The Avengers
V. Your feet (They're shoes)
I+. SCUBA
A. *Dungeons and Dragons*

545 and 546 ANSWERS

5 OR 6

T. *A New Hope*
R. The Incredible Hulk
I. The Scarlet Witch and Quicksilver
V. Smurfette
I+. *Sm*oke and f*og*
A. You stand on it (and control the game by moving your feet)

545 and 546 ANSWERS

1 OR 2

T. Which comedian starred in *The Man with Two Brains*?(2)
R. Who always tried to blow a trumpet at the beginning of *The Muppet Show*?(1)
I. Who is the editor of *The Daily Planet*?(4)
V. In the video game *Phoenix*, how many screens must you clear before you reach the Mother Ship?(6)
I+. What would you be doing if you were using a snorkel?(5)
A. What magazine is put together by "the usual gang of idiots"?(3)

QUESTIONS 551 and 552

---

3 OR 4

T. What was the title of the movie sequel to *Mad Max*?(2)
R. What alien sometimes worked for UNIT, the United Nations Intelligence Taskforce?(5)
I. What is the name of the Avengers' butler?(6)
V. How many sizes of asteroids are there in the video game *Asteroids*?(3)
I+. What is the smallest breed of dog?(4)
A. What device, which you can wear, is the Casio company noted for making?(1)

QUESTIONS 551 and 552

---

5 OR 6

T. In *E.T.*, what was the name of Elliot's sister?(5)
R. Who is the kid who starred as Arnold in *Diff'rent Strokes*?(1)
I. What does Thor always carry?(2)
V. In the video game *Phoenix*, what must you destroy that is in the Mother Ship?(3)
I+. Which is longer, a circle's diameter or its radius?(4)
A. Other than computers, what does Timex make?(6)

QUESTIONS 551 and 552

1 OR 2

T. Steve Martin
R. Gonzo
I. Perry White
V. Four
I+. Swimming
A. *MAD* magazine

551 and 552 ANSWERS

3 OR 4

T. *The Road Warrior*
R. Dr. Who
I. Jarvis
V. Three
I+. Chihuahua
A. Electronic watch

551 and 552 ANSWERS

5 OR 6

T. Gertie
R. Gary Coleman
I. His hammer
V. The Alien
I+. Its diameter
A. Watches

551 and 552 ANSWERS

1 OR 2

T. Who was Marian Ravenwood's boyfriend?(1)
R. What type of spaceship was used by the humans in *Space: 1999*?(2)
I. What color is Thor's cape?(3)
V. In the video game *Phoenix*, what happens when you shoot both wings off an attacking bird in screens three and four?(4)
I·. Name the ancient country, noted for its pyramids, where people wrote in picture symbols, or hieroglyphics.(5)
A. On appliances, what do the initials G.E. stand for?(6)

QUESTIONS 553 and 554

---

3 OR 4

T. In *Time Bandits*, where did Kevin's parents find a little bit of evil?(4)
R. What power did the Psychon called Maya have in the TV series *Space: 1999*?(3)
I. In *The Avengers* comics, who is the Mockingbird's boyfriend?(6)
V. In what video game must you defend the city of Komar from its android attackers?(5)
I·. Is a penguin a bird or a mammal?(1)
A. What appliance company is advertised by a lonely repairman?(2)

QUESTIONS 553 and 554

---

5 OR 6

T. In comic books, Lex Luthor is bald. Was he bald in the first Superman movie?(2)
R. What was the secret weapon that defeated the visitors in the television movie *V: The Final Battle*?(1)
I. What stick out from the sides of Captain America's mask?(6)
V. In the video game *Omega Race*, what happens when you hit the force field?(5)
I·. What is the closest star to our sun?(4)
A. What kind of home computer was the first to have a "freeboard" instead of a keyboard?(3)

QUESTIONS 553 and 554

1 OR 2

T. Indiana Jones
R. Eagle
I. Red
V. The birds instantly grow new wings
I+. Egypt
A. General Electric

553 and 554 ANSWERS

3 OR 4

T. In the toaster oven
R. She could change herself into an animal
I. Hawkeye
V. *Omega Race*
I+. A bird
A. Maytag

553 and 554 ANSWERS

5 OR 6

T. Yes (He wore a wig in every scene except the last)
R. Red Dust
I. Wings
V. You bounce off it
I+. Alpha Centauri
A. PCjr

553 and 554 ANSWERS

1 OR 2

T. In what movie did characters "de-rez" when they died?(5)
R. What job does Dan Rather do on television?(1)
I. What color is the Vision's skin?(4)
V. In the arcade version of *Donkey Kong*, how many screens must you clear before you get the Conveyor Belt screen?(6)
I+. What country did sombreros first come from?(3)
A. What soft drink is advertised as "clear and clean with no caffeine"?(2)

3 OR 4

T. In the *Star Wars* movies, what kind of droid could ride on the outside of an X-Wing Fighter?(1)
R. What kind of animal is Speedy Gonzales?(2)
I. What superhero group do the mutants Iceman and Angel belong to?(3)
V. In the video game *Donkey Kong*, what is the only screen in which you can't use the hammer?(5)
I+. What animal's name comes from the Greek words meaning "river horse"?(4)
A. What is the name for the special patch of black lines found on most things sold in a supermarket?(6)

5 OR 6

T. In what movie did characters have to watch out for the Recognizers?(4)
R. What character did Alan Alda play in the TV series *M*A*S*H*?(6)
I. What superhero does Mr. Mxyzptlk usually fight?(2)
V. In the video game *Donkey Kong*, what happens if you run into the big ape?(1)
I+. Is a peony a fish or a flower?(3)
A. Where will you find an anti-theft ignition lock?(5)

1 OR 2

T. *Tron*
R. Reports the news
I. Red
V. Six
I+. Mexico
A. 7-Up

555 ANSWERS

3 OR 4

T. An Artoo unit
R. A mouse
I. The New Defenders
V. Elevators (or screen four)
I+. Hippopotamus
A. U.P.C. (Universal Product Code)

555 ANSWERS

5 OR 6

T. *Tron*
R. Hawkeye Pierce
I. Superman
V. You die
I+. A flower
A. In a car

555 ANSWERS

1 OR 2

T. In *Star Wars*, how old was Chewbacca?(6)
R. What do Visitors like to eat?(1)
I. Who says "It's clobberin' time"?(2)
V. What is the largest bill in *Monopoly*?(5)
I+. What color is an avocado?(4)
A. Which friend of Strawberry Shortcake has a pet named Gooseberry?(3)

QUESTIONS 556

3 OR 4

T. What was Princess Leia's adopted last name?(6)
R. Who do Leland Snake and Ketcham Crocodile always try to make trouble for?(5)
I. Which comic-book hero is nicknamed "ol' greenskin"?(2)
V. What is the smallest bill in *Monopoly*?(1)
I+. What country are the bagpipes associated with?(3)
A. What is the name of the Smurfs' favorite cereal?(4)

QUESTIONS 556

5 OR 6

T. In *Star Wars*, what kind of a droid is See Threepio?(6)
R. What role did Emmanuel Lewis play on television, on a show of the same name?(3)
I. Which superhero is Princess of the Amazons?(1)
V. What happens if you make the wrong move playing *Curse of the Cobras*?(4)
I+. What is the word for just *one* of many bacteria?(5)
A. What kind of toothpaste fights the Cavity Creeps?(2)

QUESTIONS 556

1 OR 2

T. 200 years old
R. People
I. The Thing
V. $500
I+. Green
A. Cherry Cuddler

556 ANSWERS

---

3 OR 4

T. Organa
R. The Get Along Gang
I. The Hulk
V. $1
I+. Scotland
A. Smurfberry Crunch

556 ANSWERS

---

5 OR 6

T. A protocol droid
R. Webster
I. Wonder Woman
V. The Cobras snap shut around your arm
I+. Bacterium
A. Crest

556 ANSWERS

1 OR 2

T. In *Star Wars*, what kind of a farm did Luke Skywalker work on?(5)

R. If a voice announced that you'd just crossed over into another dimension, what old television show would you be watching?(6)

I. Who lives next door to the little girl named Sugar?(4)

V. What do the playing pieces look like in the game *On the Path to Care-A-Lot*?(3)

I+. In which country do men traditionally wear tartan kilts?(1)

A. Who is always trying to steal Ronald McDonald's hamburgers?(2)

QUESTIONS 561 and 562

3 OR 4

T. How did Han Solo get Lando Calrissian's spaceship, the *Millennium Falcon*?(4)

R. In *Donkey Kong* cartoons, what is the name of the man who is chasing after Donkey Kong?(2)

I. In *Sugar and Spike* comics, what does Sugar call Spike?(6)

V. What kind of games is the Avalon Hill company noted for making?(5)

I+. What would you find on a diamond: a faucet or a facet?(1)

A. Where can you get the burger known as the Whopper?(3)

QUESTIONS 561 and 562

5 OR 6

T. What kind of creatures were Jen and Kira in the movie *Dark Crystal*?(5)

R. In *Donkey Kong* cartoons, what is the name of the woman Donkey Kong loves?(4)

I. In *Sugar and Spike* comics, what is Sugar's last name?(6)

V. How many points do you need to win this game?(3)

I+. What is a baby deer called?(2)

A. What hamburger restaurant is identified by the Golden Arches?(1)

QUESTIONS 561 and 562

1 OR 2

T. A moisture farm
R. *The Twilight Zone*
I. Spike
V. Care Bears
I+. Scotland
A. The Hamburglar

561 and 562 ANSWERS

3 OR 4

T. Han won it
R. Mario
I. Doll-boy
V. War games
I+. Facet
A. Burger King

561 and 562 ANSWERS

5 OR 6

T. Gelflings
R. Pauline
I. Plumm
V. Thirteen
I+. Fawn
A. McDonald's

561 and 562 ANSWERS

1 OR 2

T. What was the name of the well full of snakes where Indiana Jones and Marian were trapped?(3)
R. Where was Mike Donovan when he filmed Diana eating a guinea pig?(4)
I. In *Sugar and Spike* comics, what is Spike's last name?(5)
V. Which hockey player's name appears on the game called *Rocket Hockey*?(2)
I+. Which is the shortest month?(1)
A. Which car company makes the Magic Van?(6)

QUESTIONS 563 and 564

3 OR 4

T. What did Indiana Jones hate most of all?(1)
R. What cartoon show has a zookeeper named Mr. Dinkle?(3)
I. What is the name of Dennis the Menace's dog?(2)
V. How many rockets do you get in the *G.I. Joe Cobra Battle Game*?(5)
I+. What is the name for the piece of wire that glows in a light bulb?(4)
A. Which car company makes the Fiero?(6)

QUESTIONS 563 and 564

5 OR 6

T. What was the name for the artificial humans in the movie *Blade Runner*?(5)
R. In cartoons, where does Q-Bert live?(1)
I. What is the name of the little girl Dennis the Menace keeps on giving a hard time?(2)
V. What happens when you land on a space with a question mark in *Monopoly*?(3)
I+. What kind of device is a flintlock?(4)
A. Which car company makes the 300 ZX?(6)

QUESTIONS 563 and 564

1 OR 2

T. The Well of Souls
R. On a Visitor spaceship
I. Wilson
V. Wayne Gretzky
I+. February
A. Chrysler

563 and 564 ANSWERS

3 OR 4

T. Snakes
R. *Shirt Tales*
I. Ruff
V. Ten
I+. Filament
A. General Motors

563 and 564 ANSWERS

5 OR 6

T. Replicants
R. Q-Burg
I. Margaret
V. You draw a Chance card
I+. Gun
A. Nissan (Datsun)

563 and 564 ANSWERS

1 OR 2

T. In the movie *Dragonslayer*, what kind of a creature was Vermithrax Pejorative?(1)
R. In cartoons, what school does Q-Bert go to?(5)
I. Who lives next door to Dennis the Menace?(4)
V. In *Monopoly*, what color are the Community Chest cards?(3)
I+. Is a floe hot or cold?(2)
A. Which car company makes the Corolla?(6)

QUESTIONS 565 and 566

---

3 OR 4

T. In *Dragonslayer*, who slew the dragon?(6)
R. In Q-Bert cartoons, what is the name of the bad-guy snake?(3)
I. What is Dennis the Menace's last name?(5)
V. In *Monopoly*, what color is at the top of Indiana Avenue?(1)
I+. What is the capital city of Japan?(2)
A. Which car company makes the Prelude?(4)

QUESTIONS 565 and 566

---

5 OR 6

T. In *Dragonslayer*, what was the name of the last living sorcerer?(6)
R. In Q-Bert cartoons, what is the name of the snake's girl friend?(5)
I. What are the first names of Dennis the Menace's parents?(4)
V. In *Monopoly*, what color is at the top of Pennsylvania Avenue?(1)
I+. On what kind of boat would you find a jib?(2)
A. Which chewing gum is going to move you?(3)

QUESTIONS 565 and 566

1 OR 2

T. Dragon
R. Q-Burg High
I. The Wilsons
V. Yellow
I+. Cold (It's a floating sheet of ice)
A. Toyota

565 and 566 ANSWERS

3 OR 4

T. Galen
R. Coily
I. Mitchell
V. Red
I+. Tokyo
A. Honda

565 and 566 ANSWERS

5 OR 6

T. Ulrich
R. Viper
I. Alice and Henry
V. Green
I+. A sailboat
A. Juicy Fruit

565 and 566 ANSWERS

1 OR 2

T. Which movie featured the adventures of Frodo?(5)
R. On TV, what does Donkey Kong Junior shout just before he jumps into action?(4)
I. In *Peanuts*, what does Linus wait for each year at Halloween?(1)
V. In *Monopoly*, what color is on the top of Marvin Gardens?(2)
I+. Which month was named after Julius Caesar?(3)
A. Who created the *Peanuts* cartoon strip?(6)

QUESTIONS 611 and 612

3 OR 4

T. What were the evil goblins called in the movie *The Lord of the Rings*?(1)
R. What is the name of Donkey Kong Junior's human partner?(5)
I. What is the name of Dennis the Menace's best friend?(2)
V. In *Monopoly*, what color is on top of Boardwalk?(3)
I+. Which month was named after the Roman queen of the gods, Juno?(4)
A. Who created Dennis the Menace?(6)

QUESTIONS 611 and 612

5 OR 6

T. What was the name of the good wizard in the movie *The Lord of the Rings*?(3)
R. Who is Donkey Kong Junior looking for?(1)
I. What is the name of Dennis the Menace's favorite cowboy?(4)
V. In *Monopoly*, what color is the $20 bill?(2)
I+. In a fraction, is the numerator the top number or the bottom number?(6)
A. Which comic-book company publishes The Batman and Superman comics?(5)

QUESTIONS 611 and 612

1 OR 2

T. *The Lord of the Rings*
R. "Monkey Muscle"
I. The Great Pumpkin
V. Yellow
I+. July
A. Charles Schulz

611 and 612 ANSWERS

3 OR 4

T. Orcs
R. Bones
I. Joey
V. Dark blue
I+. June
A. Hank Ketchum

611 and 612 ANSWERS

5 OR 6

T. Gandalf
R. His Dad—Donkey Kong
I. Cowboy Bob
V. Green
I+. The top
A. D.C.

611 and 612 ANSWERS

1 OR 2

T. In which movie did Ursa, Non, and General Zod try to take over the world?(3)
R. What kind of jacket did the Fonz wear?(2)
I. What does the X-Man Angel have that other people don't?(4)
V. In *Monopoly*, what do you get for passing go?(1)
I+. Which month is named for being the eighth month in the early Roman calendar?(6)
A. What comic-book company publishes *The Amazing Spider-man* and *The Fantastic Four*?(5)

QUESTIONS 613 and 614

3 OR 4

T. In *Superman*, who sentenced the Kryptonian criminals to the Phantom Zone?(5)
R. In cartoons, what is the name of Tarzan's monkey?(6)
I. Over which eye does Nick Fury have a patch?(2)
V. What do you try to do in the game *Risk*?(4)
I+. What is the national animal of the United States?(3)
A. What is the overall name for the action figures that include He-Man and Skeletor?(1)

QUESTIONS 613 and 614

5 OR 6

T. In the movie *Rocky*, what was the name of Rocky's trainer?(3)
R. In Tarzan cartoons, what kind of an animal is Numa?(5)
I. Which Inhuman can destroy things with just the sound of his voice?(6)
V. How many edges are on a Tri-Ominos playing piece?(1)
I+. If something is belated, is it early or late?(2)
A. What flying vehicle comes with Point Dread?(4)

QUESTIONS 613 and 614

1 OR 2

T. *Superman II*
R. Black leather jacket
I. Wings
V. $200
I+. October
A. Marvel

613 and 614 ANSWERS

---

3 OR 4

T. Superman's father (Jor-el)
R. Nkima
I. His left eye
V. Take over the world
I+. Bald eagle
A. Masters of the Universe

613 and 614 ANSWERS

---

5 OR 6

T. Mickey
R. A lion
I. Black Bolt
V. Three
I+. Late
A. The Talon Fighter

613 and 614 ANSWERS

1 OR 2

T. In which classic science-fiction film did Robby the Robot first appear?(5)
R. What is He-Man's real name?(D)
I. What superhero group do Elf, Rogue, and Wolverine belong to?(4)
V. In what game do you use a racquet to hit a bird?(1)
I⁺. What kind of machines use the binary number system?(2)
A. Which Masters of the Universe action figure is spring-powered?(3)

QUESTIONS 615 and 616

3 OR 4

T. In which classic science-fiction film did a computer named HAL 9000 take over a spaceship?(1)
R. What planet do the Masters of the Universe live on?(6)
I. What was the name of Captain America's original sidekick during World War II?(5)
V. What does it mean to shoot a birdie in golf?(4)
I⁺. What are the only two numerals you need to write a number in the binary number system?(2)
A. What color are the stripes on He-Man's Battle Cat?(3)

QUESTIONS 615 and 616

5 OR 6

T. In which classic science-fiction film did someone say "Gort, Klaatu barada nikto"?(6)
R. What is the name of He-Man's Battlecat?(5)
I. What comic strip features Wiley, Thor, Grog, and an anteater?(1)
V. What does it mean to shoot a bogey in golf?(4)
I⁺. What city is generally credited with being the first place to serve frankfurters?(2)
A. What Masters of the Universe vehicle has a Sky-cycle attached to it?(3)

QUESTIONS 615 and 616

1 OR 2

T. *Forbidden Planet*
R. Prince Adam
I. The X-Men
V. Badminton
I+. Computers
A. Ram Man

615 and 616 ANSWERS

---

3 OR 4

T. *2001: A Space Odyssey*
R. Eternia
I. Bucky
V. To score one less than par
I+. 0 and 1
A. Orange

615 and 616 ANSWERS

---

5 OR 6

T. *The Day the Earth Stood Still*
R. Cringer
I. *B.C.*
V. To score one more than par
I+. Frankfurt (in Germany)
A. The Battle Ram

615 and 616 ANSWERS

1 OR 2

T. What movie-monster role is Boris Karloff best remembered for?(3)
R. Who is He-Man's greatest enemy?(4)
I. In addition to Captain America, which other superhero was also injected with Super-Soldier Serum during World War II?(6)
V. What are you trying to collect with your snake in the game *Sidewinder*?(5)
I+. What does a tadpole grow into?(1)
A. How many eyes does the Masters of the Universe action figure Tri-Klops have?(2)

QUESTIONS 621 and 622

3 OR 4

T. What movie-monster role is Bela Lugosi best remembered for?(5)
R. Which of He-Man's enemies lives beneath the sea?(4)
I. In *Flash* comics, what kind of creature is Grodd?(6)
V. On what kind of table would you use a cue?(1)
I+. What is the name for the covered canoe used by the Inuit?(2)
A. Which Masters of the Universe action figure has more than one face?(3)

QUESTIONS 621 and 622

5 OR 6

T. What movie-monster role is Lon Chaney, Jr., best remembered for?(3)
R. What is the name of Skeletor's castle?(2)
I. What does The Batman have coming up from the sides of his mask?(1)
V. In what game is your piece sent to the bar if your opponent's piece lands on the same point?(4)
I+. If a king rules a kingdom, what does a queen rule?(5)
A. What kind of farm do *Star Wars* cookies come from?(6)

QUESTIONS 621 and 622

1 OR 2

T. Frankenstein's Monster
R. Skeletor
I. Nomad
V. Metal balls
I+. A frog
A. Three

621 and 622 ANSWERS

---

3 OR 4

T. Dracula
R. Mer-Man
I. A gorilla
V. A pool (or billiards) table
I+. A kayak
A. Man-E-Faces

621 and 622 ANSWERS

---

5 OR 6

T. The Wolfman
R. Castle Grayskull
I. Pointed bat ears
V. Backgammon
I+. A kingdom (Who said life was fair?)
A. Pepperidge Farm

621 and 622 ANSWERS

1 OR 2

T. What was the name of the movie that featured the defense computer WOPR?(1)
R. What is the name of the woman who fights at He-Man's side?(6)
I. In *Archie* comics, what is the name of the girl who is always after Jughead?(5)
V. In *Scrabble*, how many tiles does each player start with?(4)
I+. How many are in a quintet?(2)
A. What is the name of the collection of toy jewelry that contains a little doll in each item?(3)

QUESTIONS 623 and 624

3 OR 4

T. What did Professor Falken fly for fun in the movie *WarGames*?(5)
R. Whose forest village does King Gerard protect?(6)
I. In *Peanuts* comics, who is Lucy's brother?(1)
V. What square must be covered up in the first move in *Scrabble*?(4)
I+. How many are in a sextet?(2)
A. What comes with each My Little Pony?(3)

QUESTIONS 623 and 624

5 OR 6

T. In what theme park did *Jaws III* take place?(3)
R. What is the name of the Smurf robot?(4)
I. In *Peanuts* comics, who is Charlie Brown's sister?(1)
V. How much is the letter Y worth in *Scrabble*?(6)
I+. How many sides does a nonagon have?(5)
A. What is the most famous name in crayons?(2)

QUESTIONS 623 and 624

1 OR 2

T. *WarGames*
R. Teela
I. Big Ethel
V. Seven
I+. Five
A. Charmkins

623 and 624 ANSWERS

3 OR 4

T. A dinosaur (pterodactyl) model
R. The Smurfs'
I. Linus
V. The center square
I+. Six
A. A pet for the pony

623 and 624 ANSWERS

5 OR 6

T. Sea World
R. Clockwork
I. Sally
V. Four points
I+. Nine
A. Crayola

623 and 624 ANSWERS

1 OR 2

T. What movie showed a family's troubles getting to the theme park called Wally World?(2)
R. What weapons do He-Man and Skeletor use in their duals?(1)
I. How old is ROM, Spaceknight?(6)
V. What do you use to "roll" the die in the game *Trouble*?(5)
I+. What is a blunderbuss?(4)
A. What is the simpler version of a Lego set called?(3)

QUESTIONS 625 and 626

---

3 OR 4

T. What is the title of the Stephen King movie about a rabid St. Bernard?(5)
R. Which Smurf wears a flower on his hat?(4)
I. What is the name of ROM's fellow Spaceknight?(6)
V. In what game might Miss Scarlett have killed Colonel Mustard in the library with a candlestick?(2)
I+. What kind of weapon comes back to you if you throw it and miss your target?(1)
A. What kind of modeling material comes with a Fun Factory?(3)

QUESTIONS 625 and 626

---

5 OR 6

T. What is the title of the Stephen King movie about a killer car?(4)
R. What is the name of the Smurf who loves to eat?(2)
I. What kind of a being is ROM, Spaceknight?(6)
V. In what sport are distances measured in furlongs?(5)
I+. What do fish breathe through?(1)
A. How do you erase a Skedoodle design?(3)

QUESTIONS 625 and 626

1 OR 2

T. *National Lampoon's Vacation*
R. Power swords
I. 200 years old
V. A Pop-O-Matic
I+. A gun
A. Duplo

625 and 626 ANSWERS

---

3 OR 4

T. *Cujo*
R. Vanity
I. Starshine
V. *Clue*
I+. A boomerang
A. Play-doh

625 and 626 ANSWERS

---

5 OR 6

T. *Christine*
R. Greedy
I. A cyborg
V. Horse racing
I+. Gills
A. Turn it upside down and shake

625 and 626 ANSWERS

1 OR 2

T. What movie secret agent usually fought SPECTRE?(1)
R. What He-Man enemy is called The One-Armed Army?(4)
I. What are on the sides of the Mighty Thor's helmet?(3)
V. What is Donkey Kong called in Japan?(5)
I+. Where would you find a goatee?(6)
A. How many numbers are in a ZIP code?(2)

QUESTIONS 631 and 632

3 OR 4

T. What is the title of the Stephen King movie about a little girl who could make things catch on fire?(4)
R. In the TV show *Dungeons and Dragons*, what kind of an animal is Uni?(2)
I. Who is the Mighty Thor's father?(6)
V. What do you use to shoot insects in the video game *Centipede*?(5)
I+. Do lines of latitude run east-west or north-south?(3)
A. Where can you read the cartoon strip called *Spy vs. Spy*?(1)

QUESTIONS 631 and 632

5 OR 6

T. What movie was about the night *He* came home?(1)
R. In the TV show *Dungeons and Dragons*, what was the Magician's name?(4)
I. What mythical city does the Mighty Thor call home?(6)
V. In the video game *Centipede*, how many shots does it take to kill the flea?(5)
I+. Do lines of longitude run east-west or north-south?(3)
A. When you have your name written on a pair of mouse ears at Disneyland, does it go on the front or the back?(2)

QUESTIONS 631 and 632

1 OR 2

T. James Bond
R. Trap Jaw
I. Wings
V. Stupid Kong
I+. On a man's chin (It's a type of beard)
A. Five

631 and 632 ANSWERS

---

3 OR 4

T. *Firestarter*
R. A unicorn
I. Odin
V. The Bug Blaster
I+. East-west
A. *MAD* magazine

631 and 632 ANSWERS

---

5 OR 6

T. *Halloween*
R. Presto
I. Asgard
V. Two
I+. North-south
A. The back

631 and 632 ANSWERS

1 OR 2

T. What was the title of the Stephen King movie that was presented like a comic book?(2)
R. What character is Bobby in the TV show *Dungeons and Dragons*?(4)
I. What name did the Mighty Thor give to his enchanted hammer?(D)
V. In the video game *Centipede*, how many shots does it take to destroy a mushroom?(3)
I+. Which of the great apes has reddish hair?(1)
A. What mode does the Adam computer go into as soon as it is turned on?(5)

QUESTIONS 633 and 634

---

3 OR 4

T. What movie military group had the motto "Deeds, Not Words"?(6)
R. What character is Sheila in the TV show *Dungeons and Dragons*?(4)
I. In *Mighty Thor* comics, what is the name of the bridge that connects Earth to Asgard?(5)
V. In the video game *Centipede*, how many points is a flea worth?(3)
I+. What gas in the air is the one people must breathe to stay alive?(1)
A. Which is larger, a VHS or a Beta Cassette?(2)

QUESTIONS 633 and 634

---

5 OR 6

T. In the first *Star Trek* movie, what color was Ilia's hair?(2)
R. What character is Eric in the TV show *Dungeons and Dragons*?(4)
I. What comic-book hero does Steve Grant become when he puts on his all-white costume?(6)
V. In the video game *Centipede*, how many points is a scorpion worth?(3)
I+. What kind of animal is a Percheron?(5)
A. What brand of clothing has an alligator emblem on each item?(1)

QUESTIONS 633 and 634

1 OR 2

T. *Creepshow*
R. Barbarian
I. Mjolnir
V. Four
I+. Orangutan
A. Electronic typewriter

633 and 634 ANSWERS

---

3 OR 4

T. The Megaforce
R. Thief
I. The Rainbow Bridge
V. Two hundred
I+. Oxygen
A. A VHS cassette

633 and 634 ANSWERS

---

5 OR 6

T. She was bald (Trick question!)
R. Cavalier
I. Moon Knight
V. 1,000
I+. Horse
A. Izod

633 and 634 ANSWERS

1 OR 2

T. What was the episode number of *Return of the Jedi*?(3)
R. On *Fraggle Rock*, what is the name of the Trash Heap?(1)
I. What symbol is on the front of Moon Knight's costume?(6)
V. What Japanese company made both *Space Invaders* and *Qix*?(5)
I+. How did the people who repaired Solar Max get to work?(4)
A. How many speakers do you need to hear stereo sound?(2)

QUESTIONS 635 and 636

3 OR 4

T. How many *Star Wars* movies are there eventually supposed to be?(3)
R. On *Fraggle Rock*, who are referred to as "the silly people"?(2)
I. In what century do stories about the Legion of Super Heroes take place?(4)
V. In the video game *Qix*, what is the name for the sparkling light that chases after you along the lines you draw?(6)
I+. What is the word for the operation in which doctors take a piece of skin from one part of the body and put it on another?(5)
A. What tire company flies a blimp?(1)

QUESTIONS 635 and 636

5 OR 6

T. Who was protected by the Gamorrean Guards?(4)
R. On *Fraggle Rock*, whose workshop is outside the entrance to Outer Space?(3)
I. Which superhero group do Bouncing Boy, Brainiac Five, and Superboy belong to?(5)
V. How much of the screen do you have to block off to win a round of Qix?(6)
I+. What is hail made of?(1)
A. Who was Little Red Riding Hood visiting when she ran into the wolf?(2)

QUESTIONS 635 and 636

1 OR 2

T. Six
R. Marjorie
I. A crescent moon
V. Taito
I+. In the space shuttle *(Challenger)*
A. Two

635 and 636 ANSWERS

3 OR 4

T. Nine
R. Human beings
I. The thirtieth
V. Sparx
I+. Skin graft
A. Goodyear

635 and 636 ANSWERS

5 OR 6

T. Jabba the Hutt
R. Doc's
I. The Legion of Superheroes
V. 75% (or three-quarters)
I+. Ice
A. Her grandmother

635 and 636 ANSWERS

1 OR 2

T. What *Star Wars* hero did Mark Hamill play?(2)
R. On *Fraggle Rock*, what's the name of Doc's dog?(3)
I. Which member of the Legion of Superheroes has a twelfth-level computer mind?(6)
V. In the video game *Defender*, what happens when a Lander captures a humanoid and takes it to the top of the screen?(5)
I·. What color is a lime?(1)
A. On what kind of vehicle is a derailleur found?(4)

QUESTIONS 641 and 642

3 OR 4

T. What came from the Black Lagoon?(1)
R. Who was the captain of the *Love Boat*?(6)
I. What must people do when Wonder Woman wraps her golden rope around them?(5)
V. In the video game *Defender*, what happens when all the humanoids have been captured?(3)
I·. Are railway tracks parallel or intersecting?(2)
A. What animal does mutton come from?(4)

QUESTIONS 641 and 642

5 OR 6

T. What was the name of the fighter played by Mr. T in *Rocky III*?(3)
R. What team was Howling Mad Murdock a member of?(1)
I. What is the name of the Walt Disney puppy who has his own comic strip?(2)
V. In the video game *Defender*, what weapon destroys all the enemies on the screen at once?(4)
I·. Which country gave the Statue of Liberty to the United States?(5)
A. On what part of your body would you find your lunula?(6)

QUESTIONS 641 and 642

1 OR 2

T. Luke Skywalker
R. Sprocket
I. Brainiac Five
V. They become a mutant
I+. Green
A. A bicycle with gears

641 and 642 ANSWERS

---

3 OR 4

T. The Creature
R. Captain Merrill Stubing (Gavin MacLeod)
I. Tell the truth
V. The world explodes
I+. Parallel
A. Sheep (more than eighteen months old)

641 and 642 ANSWERS

---

5 OR 6

T. Clubber Lang
R. The A-Team
I. Scamp
V. The Smart Bomb
I+. France
A. Your finger (It's the white crescent on your fingernail)

641 and 642 ANSWERS

1 OR 2

T. What *Star Wars* hero did Carrie Fisher play?(1)
R. What were the members of the A-Team before they formed the A-Team?(5)
I. Which comic-book hero does Catwoman usually fight?(2)
V. In the video game *Defender*, how many points do you have to score to get a new Smart Bomb?(6)
I⁺. If you were in a haven, would you be safe or in trouble?(3)
A. On what part of your body would you find your septum?(4)

QUESTIONS 643 and 644

---

3 OR 4

T. What *Star Wars* hero did Anthony Daniels play?(1)
R. On what TV show did *Star Wars* characters end up on the planet Foozebane?(5)
I. Which superhero is nicknamed Hornhead?(3)
V. In *Backgammon*, how many pieces do you need on a point to block it?(2)
I⁺. How many hemispheres are there?(4)
A. Which toe is called the hallux?(6)

QUESTIONS 643 and 644

---

5 OR 6

T. What *Star Wars* hero did Kenny Baker play?(2)
R. Who is noted for saying things like "I pity the fool who doesn't know the answer to this question"?(1)
I. How does the Incredible Hulk seem to fly without having the power to fly?(4)
V. What is special about the arcade version of the video game *Sub-Roc*?(3)
I⁺. What is a group of baby kittens called?(5)
A. Which toe is called the minimus?(6)

QUESTIONS 643 and 644

1 OR 2

T. Leia
R. Commandos (or soldiers)
I. The Batman
V. 10,000
I+. Safe
A. Your nose (It's the divider between the nostrils)

643 and 644 ANSWERS

---

3 OR 4

T. See Threepio
R. *The Muppet Show*
I. Daredevil
V. Two
I+. Four (north and south, east and west)
A. The big toe

643 and 644 ANSWERS

---

5 OR 6

T. Artoo Deetoo
R. Mr. T
I. He makes powerful jumps
V. The images are three-dimensional
I+. A litter
A. The little toe

643 and 644 ANSWERS

1 OR 2

T. In what animated movie did a spider save Wilbur the Pig's life?(2)
R. In what kind of place did the show, *Barney Miller*, take place?(1)
I. In *Superman* comics, which planet is cube-shaped?(4)
V. In the video game *Scramble*, what attacks you in the cave?(3)
I·. What did the dimetrodon have growing from its back?(5)
A. What does a Geiger counter measure?(6)

QUESTIONS 645 and 646

3 OR 4

T. In *Charlotte's Web*, what kind of an animal was Templeton?(2)
R. In what kind of place does the show *WKRP in Cincinnati* take place?(1)
I. How does Jimmy Olsen call for Superman?(3)
V. In what country does the video game *Desert Flyer* take place?(5)
I·. What present day animal did the prehistoric archaeopteryx resemble?(4)
A. What science-fiction writer created the Three Laws of Robotics?(6)

QUESTIONS 645 and 646

5 OR 6

T. In *Charlotte's Web*, what kind of a creature was Charlotte?(1)
R. What is the title of the TV show that continued the story of some of the characters from *M*A*S*H*?(2)
I. In comic books, who was the original Iron Man?(3)
V. What do you call the game in which you use your open hand to hit a ball against the walls of the court?(5)
I·. Where did the prehistoric ichthyosaurus live?(4)
A. What comic-book company publishes *Wonder Woman* and *Supergirl* comics?(6)

QUESTIONS 645 and 646

1 OR 2

T. *Charlotte's Web*
R. A police station
I. The Bizarro World
V. UFOs
I+. A large fin
A. Radiation

645 and 646 ANSWERS

3 OR 4

T. A rat
R. A radio station
I. He has a special signal watch that emits a sound only Superman can hear
V. Egypt
I+. A bird
A. Isaac Asimov

645 and 646 ANSWERS

5 OR 6

T. A spider
R. *AfterM*A*S*H*
I. Anthony (Tony) Stark
V. Handball
I+. In the sea
A. D.C.

645 and 646 ANSWERS

1 OR 2

T. What was the first thing Charlotte wrote over Wilbur the Pig's stall: "Some Pig" or "Terrific"?(2)
R. Who is the host of the late night *Tonight Show*?(1)
I. In the comic book, what personal problem prevents the person who was the original Iron Man from continuing to be that superhero?(5)
V. How often are the Olympic Games held?(3)
I+. Was the allosaurus a meat-eater or a plant-eater?(4)
A. In comic books, what do the initials D.C. stand for?(6)

QUESTIONS 651 and 652

3 OR 4

T. What movie was advertised with this line: "In Space, No One Can Hear You Scream"?(1)
R. In what kind of place did the show *St. Elsewhere* take place?(2)
I. What planet is the Incredible Hulk from?(3)
V. What is the name of the sporting event that is divided into the Summer Games and the Winter Games?(5)
I+. Was the brontosaurus a meat-eater or a plant-eater?(4)
A. Which superhero was created by Joe Shuster and Jerry Siegel?(6)

QUESTIONS 651 and 652

5 OR 6

T. Which *Jaws* movie was advertised with this line: "Just when you thought it was safe to go back in the water"?(2)
R. What kind of job does the Fall Guy have?(1)
I. What color is the Green Arrow's beard?(5)
V. In what country did the Olympic Games originate?(4)
I+. Which dinosaur had a row of armor plates running along its back and spikes on its tail?(3)
A. Who created the Fantastic Four?(6)

QUESTIONS 651 and 652

1 OR 2

T. "Some Pig"
R. Johnny Carson
I. Alcoholism
V. Every four years
I+. Meat-eater
A. Detective Comics

651 and 652 ANSWERS

3 OR 4

T. *Alien*
R. A hospital
I. Earth
V. The Olympics
I+. Plant-eater
A. Superman

651 and 652 ANSWERS

5 OR 6

T. *Jaws II*
R. He's a stunt man
I. Blonde (or yellow)
V. Greece
I+. Stegosaurus
A. Stan Lee

651 and 652 ANSWERS

1 OR 2

T. What horror film did John Landis direct before he directed Thriller?(2)
R. What comic-book writer provided the narration for the *Incredible Hulk* and *Amazing Spider-man* cartoons?(4)
I. How old was Supergirl when she came to Earth?(3)
V. In the video game *Scramble*, how many points do you get for each fuel tank?(5)
I+. How many horns did the dinosaur monoclonius have?(1)
A. In the Cub Scouts, what does the word "Akela" mean?(6)

QUESTIONS 653 and 654

---

3 OR 4

T. What role did Dudley Moore play in the movie *Arthur*?(4)
R. In the British comedy show, whose Flying Circus was it?(1)
I. What superhero began as Rex Mason, Soldier of Fortune?(5)
V. In the video game *Scramble*, what happens when you destroy the enemy base?(2)
I+. What could the pteranodon do that the brontosaurus couldn't?(3)
A. What is the motto of the Cub Scouts?(D)

QUESTIONS 653 and 654

---

5 OR 6

T. Who was the lead singer for the Max Rebo Band?(2)
R. Who was Laverne's roommate?(1)
I. What does Wonder Woman use to deflect bullets?(3)
V. In *Scramble*, how many bombs can be in the air at any one time?(5)
I+. What is the proper name for the dinosaur known as the tyrant lizard?(4)
A. In the Cub Scouts, where does the word "WEBELOS" come from?(6)

QUESTIONS 653 and 654

1 OR 2

T. *An American Werewolf in London* (and one segment of *Twilight Zone: The Movie*)
R. Stan Lee
I. Fifteen
V. 150
I+. One
A. Good Leader

653 and 654 ANSWERS

3 OR 4

T. Arthur
R. Monty Python's
I. Metamorpho
V. The game begins again
I+. Fly
A. "Do your best"

653 and 654 ANSWERS

5 OR 6

T. Sy Snootles
R. Shirley
I. Her magic bracelets
V. Two
I+. Tyrannosaurus rex
A. "We'll be Loyal Scouts"

653 and 654 ANSWERS

1 OR 2

T. What was the first all-cartoon movie ever made?(6)
R. On *Shirt Tales*, what is the name of the orangutan?(1)
I. Which superhero's real name is Monica Rambeau?(5)
V. In the video game *Asteroids*, how many points is the small UFO worth?(4)
I+. In what kind of environment did the prehistoric plesiosaurus live?(2)
A. Which comic-book company publishes *Richie Rich* and *Casper* comics?(3)

QUESTIONS 655 and 656

3 OR 4

T. What kind of a shark was featured in *Jaws*?(1)
R. On *Shirt Tales*, what is the name of the panda?(2)
I. What superhero group does Magneto usually fight?(3)
V. In the video game *Asteroids*, how many points is the large UFO worth?(4)
I+. Which of these was a flying dinosaur: brachiosaurus, saltoposuchus, or rhamphorhynchus?(6)
A. Which comic-book company publishes *Archie* comics?(5)

QUESTIONS 655 and 656

5 OR 6

T. What was the first thing we saw the Rancor Beast eat in *Return of the Jedi*?(4)
R. On *Shirt Tales*, what is the name of the tiger?(3)
I. What is printed on the front of the Fantastic Four's uniforms?(1)
V. In the video game *Asteroids*, how many points are the small asteroids worth?(5)
I+. Which of these was a swimming dinosaur: geosaur, diplodocus, or ornitholestes?(6)
A. In the Ghostbusters computer game what do you have to do to hear a voice say, "Ghostbusters"?(2)

QUESTIONS 655 and 656

1 OR 2

T. *Snow White and the Seven Dwarfs*
R. Bogey
I. Captain Marvel
V. 1,000
I·. Water
A. Harvey Comics

655 and 656 ANSWERS

3 OR 4

T. A great white shark
R. Pammy
I. The X-Men
V. 200
I·. Rhamphorhynchus
A. The Archie Comics Group

655 and 656 ANSWERS

5 OR 6

T. A Gammorean guard (We didn't see it eat Jabba's first "pet")
R. Tyg
I. The number 4
V. One hundred
I·. Geosaur
A. Press the space bar

655 and 656 ANSWERS

1 OR 2

T. In *Superman II*, how many men had superpowers?(1)
R. On *Shirt Tales*, what is the name of the raccoon?(2)
I. How does Superman manage to travel through time?(6)
V. In the video game *Joust*, what lives in the lava?(3)
I+. What continent do llamas live on?(5)
A. What cereal does the Honey Nut Bee advertise?(4)

QUESTIONS 661 and 662

---

3 OR 4

T. Who starred in *Stroker Ace*?(4)
R. On *Shirt Tales*, what was the name of the possum?(1)
I. What superhero group does the Brotherhood of Evil Mutants usually fight?(2)
V. In the video game *Joust*, what kind of monster is called "unbeatable"?(3)
I+. Where in your body would you find your medulla oblongata?(6)
A. What is the name of the toy cars that can jump over obstacles?(5)

QUESTIONS 661 and 662

---

5 OR 6

T. In *Friday the 13th*, who jumped onto the canoe?(2)
R. What is the title of the only TV movie ever made by Steven Spielberg?(6)
I. How does Superman shave his indestructible beard?(5)
V. In the video game *Dragon's Lair*, what happens after you successfully complete the game?(4)
I+. In what piece of computer equipment might you find a daisy wheel?(1)
A. In *The Hobbit*, what was Gollum's precious?(3)

QUESTIONS 661 and 662

1 OR 2

T. Three
R. Ricky
I. He flies faster than the speed of light
V. The Fire Troll
I+. South America
A. Honey Nut Cheerios

661 and 662 ANSWERS

---

3 OR 4

T. Burt Reynolds
R. Digger
I. The X-Men
V. A pterodactyl
I+. In your head (It's the lowest part of your brain)
A. Jumpsters

661 and 662 ANSWERS

---

5 OR 6

T. Jason
R. *Duel*
I. He burns it off with his heat vision reflected in a mirror
V. The game ends (No new rounds, no extra Dirks)
I+. Printer
A. The Ring

661 and 662 ANSWERS

1 OR 2

T. Which movie was advertised with this line: "You will believe a man can fly"?(3)
R. What TV show featured the character Johnny Fever?(4)
I. Which cartoon cat loves lasagna?(1)
V. What kind of vehicle do you control in the arcade game *Spy Hunter*?(2)
I+. What is brine: water with salt or water with sugar?(5)
A. Which home video-game company has the home rights to *Dragon's Lair*?(6)

QUESTIONS 663 and 664

3 OR 4

T. In *WarGames*, what was the name of the computer's talking program?(5)
R. On *Fraggle Rock*, what kind of vegetables does Junior Gorg have on his pajamas?(6)
I. In *Peanuts* cartoons, what does Marcia always call Peppermint Patti?(4)
V. In what video game are you attacked by tires and dice and ice-cream sandwiches and irons and just about everything else?(3)
I+. What is butter made from?(1)
A. Who created the *Star Wars* saga?(2)

QUESTIONS 663 and 664

5 OR 6

T. What is the title of the film about the early days of the American space program?(3)
R. Who were the warlike aliens in *Star Trek*?(4)
I. In *Peanuts* cartoons, what does Peppermint Patti always call Charlie Brown?(5)
V. Is the *Star Wars* video arcade game done in vector graphics or raster graphics?(2)
I+. In Greek legend, what is a centaur?(6)
A. How many pennies equal one dollar?(1)

QUESTIONS 663 and 664

1 OR 2

T. *Superman*
R. *WKRP in Cincinnati*
I. Garfield
V. Car
I+. Water with salt
A. Coleco

663 and 664 ANSWERS

3 OR 4

T. Joshua
R. Radishes
I. Sir
V. *Megomania*
I+. Cream (or milk)
A. George Lucas

663 and 664 ANSWERS

5 OR 6

T. *The Right Stuff*
R. Klingons
I. Chuck
V. Vector graphics
I+. A half-human, half-horse creature
A. One hundred

663 and 664 ANSWERS

1 OR 2

T. In what movie did the evil Skeksis try to kill the innocent Gelflings?(3)
R. What was the name of the helicopter in *Riptide*?(6)
I. What does the X-Man, Storm, have power over?(4)
V. What comic strip is featured in the video game *Quest for Tires*?(1)
I+. Would a chandelier be on a ceiling or in a small Italian boat?(2)
A. What sort of things does the company called Don Post Studios make?(5)

QUESTIONS 665 and 666

---

3 OR 4

T. What movie featured a person who could talk to animals?(1)
R. What does the hero of *Magnum, P.I.* do for a living?(4)
I. In *Superboy* comics, which friend of Clark Kent knows that he is really Superboy?(6)
V. What is the name of the second video arcade game based on *Tron*?(5)
I+. What modern-day animal resembles an extinct mammoth, but without fur?(3)
A. How many states are in the United States?(2)

QUESTIONS 665 and 666

---

5 OR 6

T. What planet did the Death Star destroy in *Star Wars*?(2)
R. What is the name of the half-human, half-alien child on *V*?(3)
I. What country does the X-Man, Colossus, come from?(4)
V. What video game company made *Pole Position*?(1)
I+. What kind of tree grows from an acorn?(5)
A. In the last book they appeared in, what did Steve "Clubber" Heaslip and Campbell "Howling Mad" Kingsburgh turn into?(D)

QUESTIONS 665 and 666

1 OR 2

T. *The Dark Crystal*
R. *Screaming Mimi*
I. The weather
V. *B.C.*
I+. A ceiling
A. Masks and makeup

665 and 666 ANSWERS

3 OR 4

T. *Doctor Dolittle*
R. He's a private investigator
I. Pete Ross
V. *Discs of Tron*
I+. The elephant
A. Fifty

665 and 666 ANSWERS

5 OR 6

T. Alderaan
R. Elizabeth
I. Russia
V. Atari
I+. Oak
A. Vampires

665 and 666 ANSWERS

SCORESHEETS

The Scoresheets on the next four pages are designed for use with this book. For best results, photocopy a small supply or use them as a guide and write the letters **T.R.I.V.I+.A.** down a sheet of paper three times for each player.

PLAYER____________

T.____ T.____ T.____

R.____ R.____ R.____

I.____ I.____ I.____

V.____ V.____ V.____

I+.____ I+.____ I+.____

A.____ A.____ A.____

PLAYER____________

T.____ T.____ T.____

R.____ R.____ R.____

I.____ I.____ I.____

V.____ V.____ V.____

I+.____ I+.____ I+.____

A.____ A.____ A.____

PLAYER____________

T.____ T.____ T.____

R.____ R.____ R.____

I.____ I.____ I.____

V.____ V.____ V.____

I+.____ I+.____ I+.____

A.____ A.____ A.____

PLAYER____________

T.____ T.____ T.____

R.____ R.____ R.____

I.____ I.____ I.____

V.____ V.____ V.____

I+.____ I+.____ I+.____

A.____ A.____ A.____

PLAYER____________ PLAYER____________

T.____ T.____ T.____ T.____ T.____ T.____

R.____ R.____ R.____ R.____ R.____ R.____

I.____ I.____ I.____ I.____ I.____ I.____

V.____ V.____ V.____ V.____ V.____ V.____

I+.____ I+.____ I.+.____ I+.____ I+.____ I+.____

A.____ A.____ A.____ A.____ A.____ A.____

PLAYER____________ PLAYER____________

T.____ T.____ T.____ T.____ T.____ T.____

R.____ R.____ R.____ R.____ R.____ R.____

I.____ I.____ I.____ I.____ I.____ I.____

V.____ V.____ V.____ I.____ V.____ V.____

I+.____ I+.____ I+.____ I+.____ I+.____ I+.____

A.____ A.____ A.____ A.____ A.____ A.____

PLAYER________________ PLAYER________________

T.____	T.____	T.____	T.____	T.____	T.____
R.____	R.____	R.____	R.____	R.____	R.____
I.____	I.____	I.____	I.____	I.____	I.____
V.____	V.____	V.____	V.____	V.____	V.____
I+.____	I+.____	I+.____	I+.____	I+.____	I+.____
A.____	A.____	A.____	A.____	A.____	A.____

PLAYER________________ PLAYER________________

T.____	T.____	T.____	T.____	T.____	T.____
R.____	R.____	R.____	R.____	R.____	R.____
I.____	I.____	I.____	I.____	I.____	I.____
V.____	V.____	V.____	V.____	V.____	V.____
I+.____	I+.____	I+.____	I+.____	I+.____	I+.____
A.____	A.____	A.____	A.____	A.____	A.____

PLAYER______________

T.____ T.____ T.____

R.____ R.____ R.____

I.____ I.____ I.____

V.____ V.____ V.____

I+.____ I+.____ I+.____

A.____ A.____ A.____

PLAYER______________

T.____ T.____ T.____

R.____ R.____ R.____

I.____ I.____ I.____

V.____ V.____ V.____

I+.____ I+.____ I+.____

A.____ A.____ A.____

PLAYER______________

T.____ T.____ T.____

R.____ R.____ R.____

I.____ I.____ I.____

V.____ V.____ V.____

I+.____ I+.____ I+.____

A.____ A.____ A.____

PLAYER______________

T.____ T.____ T.____

R.____ R.____ R.____

I.____ I.____ I.____

V.____ V.____ V.____

I+.____ I+.____ I+.____

A.____ A.____ A.____

Using ULTIMATE TRIVIA Questions with Your Other Favorite Trivia Games

To make this book into a set of game cards, you will need an adult to help you cut it apart. The adult will need a metal-edge ruler and an art or hobby knife.

C

Art knives are very sharp and can be dangerous! Get an adult to follow these instructions carefully.

A

---

1. Cut off the back cover.
2. Hold the ruler along line A and gently cut with the knife. It's a good idea to keep the book on some heavy cardboard to prevent cutting through to a tabletop. Cut slowly and gently. Don't try to go through too many pages at once.
3. After the top third of the book has been cut through, repeat step 2 for line B.

C

B

---

4. When the book is in thirds, remove the spine from each section by cutting along line C.

C

You now have 336 new game-cards adaptable to most other popular trivia games.